Books are to be returned on or before
the last date below.

HELICOPTERS
at War

HELICOPTERS
at War

Blitz Editions

This edition published in 1996 by:
Blitz Editions
an imprint of Bookmart Limited
Registered Number 2372865
Trading as Bookmart Limited
Desford Road
Enderby
Leicester LE9 5AD

ISBN 1 85605 345 8

Editorial and design: Brown Packaging Limited,
255–257 Liverpool Road, London N1 1LX

Printed in the Slovak Republic
60155

*Photograph page 2: The AH-1W Super Cobra, as used by the
US Marines.*

CONTENTS

APACHE
on the warpath

Below: The pilot of an Apache has a formidable array of sensors to help him. The green disc on the side of his helmet swings over to cover his right eye, enabling him to fire his guns wherever he looks.

Above: Looking like a huge mechanical insect, the Apache carries Hellfire missiles and rocket pods to attack tanks and soft targets respectively. Its sensors allow it to shoot accurately at night.

Flying fast and low over the battlefield, the Apache helicopter gunship can destroy any tank in the world. Day or night, in smoke or through fog, it makes no difference. This $10-million killing machine has a formidable array of sensors and guided missiles that find their own way to the target. The AH-64 Apache is the first purpose-built all-weather tank-killing helicopter to enter service with the US Army. Costing more than five times as much as the Soviet tanks it was designed to destroy, the Apache

Above: An Apache fires 2.75-in rockets from the pods on each weapons pylon. A hail of rockets like this persuaded one Iraqi battalion to surrender to the Apaches bombarding its position.

Above: The Apache's gunner sits in the front seat surrounded by target acquisition, laser and weapon systems. He can kill enemy targets up to 6 km distant in all weathers, at night and in the smokescreens of battle.

Below: An Apache banks to display its eight Hellfire missiles. Apaches rely on the long range of their missiles and their ability to manoeuvre around terrain features to avoid enemy fire. Although their armour will stop some projectiles, they cannot afford to take repeated hits from anti-aircraft guns.

came in for a lot of criticism in the early days of its career. But its ability to hit pinpoint targets in the dead of night was demonstrated during the 1989 invasion of Panama.

In Operation 'Desert Storm', the Apache gunships slaughtered the Iraqi armoured columns retreating from Kuwait City. Just before the ground offensive began, an entire Iraqi battalion surrendered to the Apache squadron attacking it. The Apaches hovered over the prisoners until Chinook transport helicopters could arrive and take the Iraqis to PoW camps.

Night fighting

The US Army did have an attack helicopter, the AH-1 Cobra, during the 1970s but this could not fight at night nor in bad weather. The Apache is fitted with the TADS/PNVS system, which keeps it fighting right around the clock. TADS (Target Acquisition and Designation Sight) incorporates infra-red direct optics and television system in a nose turret. This allows the co-pilot/gunner to locate targets in all weathers, after which a laser can be used to designate an enemy tank on which guided missiles can be homed in with devastating accuracy.

Above the TADS is the PNVS (Pilot Night Vision System), a forward-looking infra-red scanner that allows the pilot to fly at low level in pitch darkness. Both crew members wear a helmet which is linked to the helicopter's sensors and weapons: merely by turning their heads, the crew can direct the sensors at a target area.

Having located and locked-on to its target, the Apache has three main weapons to unleash. By far the most important is the Hellfire anti-tank missile. This is laser-guided and, provided the target is constantly 'sparkled' by a laser designator, Hellfire will home-in on the reflected laser energy bouncing off the enemy tank and blow it to pieces. The target can be laser-designated by soldiers on the ground or light scout helicopters so that the Apache can engage another target the moment it has fired its Hellfire.

Inside the Apache

The most sophisticated attack helicopter in the world, the McDonnell Douglas AH-64A Apache is a carefully-integrated weapon system combining superb offensive capability and high survivability in the face of present and projected Soviet defences. It is one of the West's most important anti-armour asset.

Cockpit

Apache's pilot sits above and behind the co-pilot/gunner. In many ways, the crewmen are the most fragile parts of the Apache, and they are very well protected. The cockpit floor is a special kind of armour made from boron. Both crew seats have Kevlar armour behind and to the sides, proof against heavy machine-gun and light cannon fire.

TADS/PNVS sensors

At the heart of the Apache's outstanding performance is the TADS/PNVS swivelling turret in the nose. The top unit is the Pilot's Night Vision System (PNVS), an infra-red sensor which allows the pilot to see at night and in bad weather. Below that are the multiple sensors of the Target Acquisition and Designation System (TADS), which include telescopic direct view optical sights, a low-light television camera, a laser rangefinder and designator, and a forward-looking infra-red system which can detect targets on the darkest night.

Hellfire missile

Hellfire is an acronym derived from 'Helicopter-launch, fire-and-forget'. The supersonic missile is the fastest, most powerful and most effective hell-launched anti-tank missile in service today. The current version is a laser-homer, its nose-mounted seeker guiding the missile in the 'sparkle' created by a laser beam directed onto the target.

Weapons load

Although Hellfire is the Apache's main weapon, the aircraft also carries folding-fin air-launched rockets. The M261 lightweight launcher contains 19 2.75-in high-explosive rockets. Apache can also be armed with Sidewinder and Stinger air-to-air missiles.

Powerplant

Apache is powered by two General Electric T700-GE-701 turboshaft engines, each of 1,723 shp maximum power. They are mounted in armour-plated pods on each side of the fuselage, above the stub wings. The engine cowlings hinge downwards and can serve as platforms for maintenance crews.

Construction

The fuselage of the Apache is of conventional aircraft aluminium construction, but more strongly made so as to be able to stand up to direct hits from Soviet 23-mm cannon shells. Controls and control surfaces are duplicated and separated wherever possible, so that damage to one set will not knock out the other and leave the aircraft out of control.

Ammunition

High Explosive and High Explosive Dual Purpose (armour piercing) ammunition for the M230 Chain Gun is kept in a tray directly beneath the rotor. It holds 1,200 rounds of NATO standard 30-mm ammunition, and is connected to the gun by a conveyor system beneath the cockpit.

M230 30-mm Chain Gun

The Chain Gun can fire 30-mm cannon shells from single shots up to a rate of 625 rounds per minute. The weapon's primary function is to suppress enemy defences while the helicopter is attacking armour with missiles. The gun is slaved to the crew's helmet sights: it points to whatever the pilot or the gunner look at.

Countermeasures

Heat-seeking missiles can be fooled if you present their simple 'brains' with an alternative heat source. Apaches are fitted with small boxes just in front of the tail assembly that eject flares. These burn fiercely, decoying missiles away from the helicopter.

Tail rotor

Apache has two separate tail rotor blades set in a flattened 'X', which produces much less noise than conventional tail rotors set at right angles.

Tail assembly

Drive for the tail rotor comes from the main gearbox, via drive shafts down the rear fuselage, bending up the rotor pylon to the right-angle final drive gearbox. Apache has a one-piece, all-moving tailplane, the angle of which influences the helicopter's speed.

Exhaust suppression

The sky over a modern battlefield will be a hostile place for helicopters. One of the most deadly weapons will be heat-seeking missiles, so the exhaust ducts at the back of each of the Apache's two engines are designed to cool the hot gases from the gas-turbine engines.

Main rotor

Each of the four rotor blades is fully articulated, being attached to the massive rotor hub by a pair of hinges that allow the blades to twist and flap up and down. The blades themselves are complex structures of steel and honeycomb composite material, which can withstand direct hits from Soviet 23-mm cannon shells.

Apaches carry up to 16 Hellfires, but the standard load is eight. The outer wing pylons are usually filled by a 19-round 2.75-in rocket pod. This is highly effective against infantry targets or unarmoured vehicles like the truck columns caught on the Basra-Kuwait City highway.

Under the nose, the Apache carries a 30-mm Chain Gun slaved to the sighting system with powered elevation and traverse. This fires at a rate of 625 rounds per minute. Capable of penetrating the top armour of all but a few types of tank, the Chain Gun chews up lightly armoured infantry

Above: A Hellfire is launched. Because Hellfire missiles are laser-guided, Apaches can drop back into cover if another helicopter or a ground unit is designating the target with a laser.

fighting vehicles with devastating effect.

Because the Apache can fire its missiles from beyond the range of light anti-aircraft weapons and even the quadruple 23-mm cannon used by the Soviet forces, the best defence against an Apache is another gunship. The Soviets have already built two similar helicopters, so the Apache is now being fitted with air-to-air missiles.

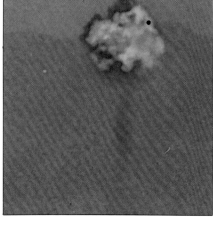

Above: Although Hellfire is primarily for attacking tanks, this missile has just struck an aircraft drone target in mid-air. If enemy helicopters are a threat, the Apache can carry infra-red homing air-to-air missiles.

Apache Warriors blast Iraqis EYEWITNESS

"This battalion was credited as the first attack helicopter battalion ever to take prisoners. We engaged an Iraqi infantry battalion 100 km inside Iraq, and shot them with the 30-mm gun to get them stopped. The Iraqis dismounted, then we fired three Hellfires and took out their lead vehicles. From that point on we finished them off with 30-mm and the 2.75-inch rocket. After about five hours of that we got a leaflet team in with an Arabic speaker and a PA system. He offered them safe passage and they all surrendered. We captured 476 Iraqi soldiers.

"The sector we were in was far out to the west. As the 101st Airborne Division advanced, we pushed out another 50 km to the Euphrates river. Iraqi forces realised they were being bypassed and fled north. But once they saw armed helicopters appear, they immediately got out of their vehicles and took cover. It turned out that the Iraqis didn't have the resolve to fight, although they certainly had the equipment. We found enormous amounts of anti-aircraft weapons and missile systems.

"On the 27th we did a classic deep attack, moved over 300 km to attack a Republican Guard division attempting to escape. We engaged primarily with Hellfire although we did shoot some 2.75- and 30-mm. There were hundreds of vehicles — our battalion took out 50 or 60: BMPs, BM21 rocket

launchers, trucks, BRDMs etc. It was just chaos. We were engaged by several heat-seeking missiles, SA-6s I think, but there were so many fires, so much smoke that none of them could acquire and hit us."

**Lt Col Bill Bryan, 'Bengal 6',
2nd Battalion/229th Aviation Regiment,
based in Saudi Arabia and Iraq during
Operation Desert Storm.**

Two Sidewinder or four Stinger infra-red homing missiles will make the Apache a very dangerous opponent for enemy jets or helicopters.

Because it is designed to attack heavily-armed tank formations, the Apache is built to take punishment. Many systems are duplicated in case of damage, and the crew seats and transmission are protected by Kevlar and ESR (Electro-Slag Remelt) steel. The rotor blades can keep going even after direct hits from 23-mm cannon shells. If an enemy anti-aircraft missile system achieves a radar lock-on, a warning device alerts the crew. The Apache can break it by firing chaff — strips of aluminium foil that blanket a radar screen and mask the helicopter's position. The Apache's exhaust is suppressed to offer heat-seeking missiles less of a target.

The Apache was built as part of NATO's defence against the enormous tank forces of the USSR. In the Gulf War it spearheaded the low-level air assault in advance of allied forces. In attack or defence, the Apache is a formidable weapon system indeed.

The AH-1 Cobra was the world's first dedicated gunship helicopter. It introduced the fighter-style, two-man, tandem cockpit which is now the norm for attack machines, as well as the powerful gun and rocket armament.

THE DEADLY COBRA

Squatting in a foxhole, you can hear the rumble of approaching armour above the noise of battle and a distant chop-chop of rotor blades. A bright light flashes across the sky above your retreat, followed by a distant thud. The rumble ceases, and a Cobra appears from the trees behind you, gun turret traversing the treeline beyond you for signs of movement.

Clinical killing power

As the helicopter manoeuvres into open ground, two small flashes of gunfire spring from the treeline. The gun turret spews a two-second burst into the vegetation, raking a 20-yard section. There are no more muzzle flashes. As you marvel at the clinical killing power of this fearsome brute, it is gone, lifting its tail so that the rotor blades nearly hit the ground in front of it, accelerating from a walking pace to over 100 knots in a few seconds.

Such is the game of the Bell Model 209, designated the AH-1 by the US Army but universally known as the Cobra. Its job now is to provide fire support and attack enemy armour, but 25 years ago when it entered service it hunted Vietnamese communists in the jungles and forests of South East Asia.

Early successes in the Vietnam War with heavily-armed Bell UH-1 Hueys

A Cobra from a US Army cavalry regiment escorts a convoy of APCs. Army Cobras are identifiable by the flat armoured glass around their cockpits.

led Bell to develop a specialist gunship version which employed many of the components of the Huey, attached to a new, sleek fuselage. Pilot and gun-

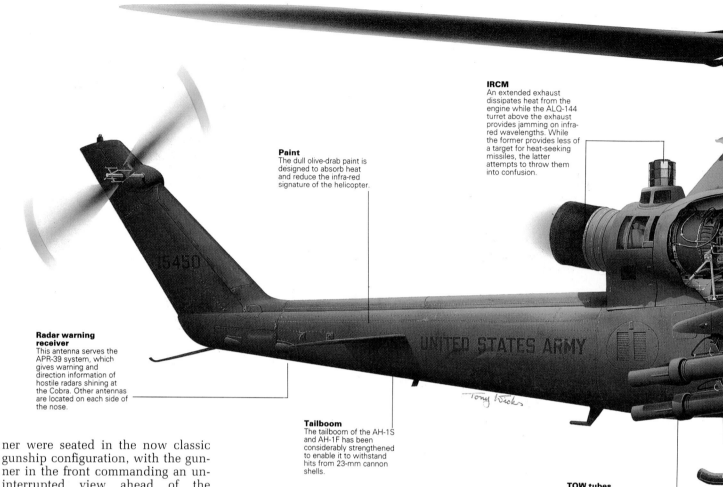

IRCM
An extended exhaust dissipates heat from the engine while the ALQ-144 turret above the exhaust provides jamming on infra-red wavelengths. While the former provides less of a target for heat-seeking missiles, the latter attempts to throw them into confusion.

Paint
The dull olive-drab paint is designed to absorb heat and reduce the infra-red signature of the helicopter.

Radar warning receiver
This antenna serves the APR-39 system, which gives warning and direction information of hostile radars shining at the Cobra. Other antennas are located on each side of the nose.

Tailboom
The tailboom of the AH-1S and AH-1F has been considerably strengthened to enable it to withstand hits from 23-mm cannon shells.

TOW tubes
TOW tubes and their missiles come in modules of two, four modules being the usual load for the AH-1. After launch, fins pop out to stabilise the missile in flight.

ner were seated in the now classic gunship configuration, with the gunner in the front commanding an uninterrupted view ahead of the machine. With tandem seating, the designers achieved a very small frontal cross-section, making the helicopter an extremely small target from head-on. Weapons were to be carried under two stub wings attached to the side of the fuselage, and in a chin turret.

Development ran quickly, and in 1967 the first examples of the AH-1G reached Vietnam, after the type's first flight in September 1965. Deliveries were swift to the theatre, and the AH-1 soon proved itself as one of the most important weapons operating in South East Asia. Combat operations often included fire support of ground forces, whereby ground commanders could call up the gunships when they faced superior forces. Helicopter escort was another major role, the Cobras riding 'shotgun' to the troop-carrying Hueys until a few miles short of their LZ, when they would speed ahead and soften up the LZ, making it safe for the 'slicks' to land.

Weapon fits were many, with the chin turret able to take either two 7.62-mm machine-guns or 40-mm grenade launchers, or one of each. Further gun pods could be carried under the stub wings, in addition to rocket pods. While most served with the Army, others went to the Marine Corps, which eventually received its

The Cobra is air-transportable with a minimum of fuss, easily accommodated by the Lockheed C-5 Galaxy, allowing rapid deployment to any spot on the globe.

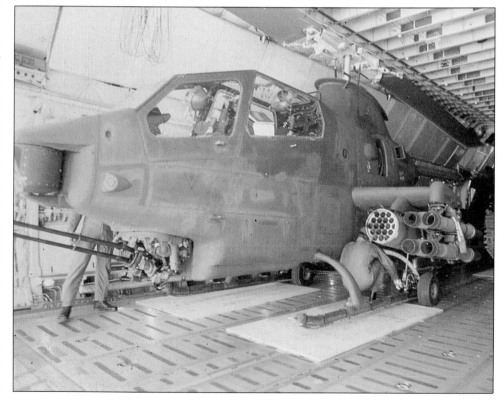

Laser tracker
This blister hides a laser spot tracker, which enables the Cobra to locate targets designated by other friendlies.

Air data probe
For updating the sighting system with accurate atmospheric data, this sensor is mounted well away from the disturbed airflow around the fuselage.

Inside the Cobra

This aircraft is in the fully-upgraded US Army AH-1F configuration, incorporating all the modifications of recent years. It is shown in the typical battlefield weapons fit, with TOW missiles for armoured targets and 2.75-in rocket pods and 20-mm cannon for soft targets.

Sight
This sight provides the gunner with a magnified thermal imaging system for TOW launch. Laser augmentation provides accurate range information.

Cannon
The M197 three-barrel 20-mm rotary cannon can fire up to 3,000 rounds per minute, with a magazine capacity of 750 rounds. Aiming is either from helmet sights (both crew) or from the TOW sight.

Canopy
The flat-pane armoured windows are designed to prevent glinting which might give away the Cobra's position. Explosives jettison the door in emergency for rapid egress.

Wire cutter
Above and below the forward fuselage are blades to cut cables if the helicopter collides with them.

Rocket pod
For area denial work the principal weapon is the M159 rocket pod, which can carry 19 FFARs (Folding-Fin Aircraft Rocket) of 2.75-in calibre.

twin-engined AH-1J version in 1970, this variant being considered safer for over-water operations.

With the Vietnam War over, Bell developed the Cobra for the anti-armour role, although the aircraft was still able to perform its previous roles. The main modification lay in the adoption of the TOW anti-tank missile, of which eight could be carried under the stub wings. So equipped, the first TOW Cobras were designated AH-1Q, followed by the AH-1R which featured an uprated engine but no TOW capability. Finally the AH-1S brought both modifications together.

Even so, AH-1S aircraft have existed in many different configurations, and the shape of the Cobra has evolved to incorporate a new chin turret with a three-barrel 20-mm cannon, an angular flat-pane canopy, infra-red countermeasures turret and various infra-red suppressors on the exhaust. The first of these was an upturned unit, but now a special suppressor has been added to the exhaust.

During the mid-1980s, the fully

modernised AH-1S aircraft were designated AH-1F, and the US Army hopes to modernise all its fleet to this standard, although many AH-1S helicopters exist in lesser stages of conversion. The Marine Corps too has introduced better models, the first being the AH-1T with uprated engine and dynamic system, which soon gained TOW capability. In the late 1980s they received AH-1W aircraft with even greater power and new weapons options such as the Sidewinder air-to-air missile.

Both Army and Marine Corps Cobras saw extensive action in the Gulf War, and Iranian AH-1Js were used in the Iran-Iraq War. Israeli Cobras were used against the Syrians in 1982 and many times since in the Lebanon. Other AH-1 operators include Japan, Jordan, Pakistan and South Korea.

Scout helicopters provide the Cobra with much of its targeting information. In current use with the US Army is the Bell OH-58 Kiowa, shown here with an AH-1F.

So how does the Cobra operate in the anti-armour role? For delivery of its principal weapon, the TOW missile, it utilises a Laser Augmented Airborne TOW sight mounted in the extreme nose. This sight allows the gunner to spot targets at long range, and then guide the TOW missile by thermal imaging on to the target. Laser augmentation is provided by designators situated either on the ground or more likely in an airborne scout helicopter such as the Bell OH-58D, which 'spots' the target with a laser. This shows in the gunner's sight, allowing him to guide the missile from far greater ranges than if he were using purely optical sighting.

With the four-round TOW launcher occupying the outer pylon on each wing, the inner pylon can be used primarily for 2.75-in rocket pods, available in seven- or 19-tube versions. These weapons are aimed in a shallow dive, as usually is the chin gun. Both rockets and gun are used for fire support of friendly troops, and, due to the normal attack profile, are used in areas away from intense groundfire.

Helicopters are vulnerable wherever they can be clearly seen, so it is better for the Cobra to operate from cover as much as possible. Ingress and egress are made at below treetop height, the aircraft popping-up above just to acquire, aim and guide the TOW missiles. To avoid attack, the AH-1F is fitted with a radar warning receiver and an infra-red countermeasures turret behind the rotor mast. Armour is incorporated into the aircraft around the cockpit. In the future Cobras will be configured to carry air-to-air missiles to defend themselves or to act as fighters over the battlefield, taking on both enemy aircraft and helicopters.

The most recent production model of the Cobra is the Marine Corps AH-1W Super Cobra. It has more powerful engines, and like the US Army's AH-64 Apache it can fire Hellfire laser-guided anti-armour missiles. Marine Corps AH-1s are also configured to fire air-to-air missiles, but this is primarily a defensive measure since their main function remains the close support of Marine assaults. Based on assault carriers alongside Boeing Vertol CH-46 Sea Knight troopers, the AH-1s would escort helicopters and landing craft during the initial assault, and then support the Marines once ashore at the beachhead.

Although nowhere near so sophisticated as the McDonnell Douglas AH-64 Apache now in service, the Cobra is still a highly valued asset on the battlefield, and available in such large numbers that its impact on any armoured conflict remains huge. Despite being over 20 years old, the airframe has plenty of room for improvement: certainly the adoption of a roof- or mast-mounted sight would render it less vulnerable in the face of heavy defences. One of the great successes of the Vietnam War, Bell's Cobra is still in business, and will be so for years to come.

Cobras often operate in fire teams with spotting helicopters. Here, a 'Snake' comes in to land behind an OH-58D scout helicopter during the last phase of the Gulf War.

ON THE OFFENSIVE

The Honeywell IHADSS (Integrated Helmet and Display Sight System) has an electro-optical system which provides flight information and data on targets in the glass over your right eye.

5 POINTS FOR A SUCCESSFUL OPERATION

1. Aggression and initiative.
2. Rapid shifts in the main effort to take advantage of opportunities.
3. The deepest, most rapid destruction of enemy defences.
4. Quick shifting of strength to widen penetration of enemy defensive zone and reinforce successful attacks.
5. Probing attacks to identify enemy weak points or gaps into which the main assault can be made.

You have to move fast in attack, especially when you're at the controls of an attack helicopter. You've got the firepower, you've got the range, the endurance, the speed and manoeuvrability. Top that off with your own hunting instincts, and the whole package adds up to one of the most formidable weapons on the modern field of battle.

Attacking a defended position when the enemy knows you're coming is an expensive and dangerous business. The defender has great advantages: the main one is that he has chosen the place.

Pick your moment

But he has a big disadvantage, too – he doesn't choose the time. You do. And you make sure that you use that edge to the best possible effect by concentrating your combat power at the points where the defence is weakest.

By using surprise, concentration of forces and out-and-out aggression, an attack can succeed even though the odds may be against it. Attack helicopters are the best possible vehicle for this sort of offensive.

Tailor your movement to the terrain, using concealment techniques like contour following and Nap-Of-the-Earth (NOE) flying. Use supporting fire and suppression techniques, but above all, know your enemy. How is he equipped? What is his main threat? How well does he use the kit he's got?

These things add up to the effective range of his anti-aircraft fire. If the

Suppressing the enemy with a hail of 70-mm rockets, an AH-64 Apache swoops in to the attack. In offensive operations one of the main missions of the attack helicopter is to gain or re-establish contact with fast-moving enemy forces. This demands rapid movement, decentralised control and the ability to organise hasty attacks against opportunity targets.

A US Army AH-64 Apache flies over the desert, keeping well above the ground where fine sand kicked up by the rotorwash betrays the helicopter's position.

ASSEMBLY AREAS AND HOLDING AREAS

In the rear of the fighting front, far enough back to be out of range of enemy medium artillery, the attack helicopter units will establish an assembly area where they can rest and resupply.

The closer to the fighting front the assembly area has to be established, the sparser will be the range of combat support services available, until we reach the point where only the attack helicopters and their crews are present. By that time the assembly area has turned into a holding area.

You choose an assembly area according to these considerations:
1 Entry and exit routes
2 Cover and concealment
3 Space
4 Proximity to friendly units
5 Proximity to main supply routes
6 Security

Helicopters flying in and out of the same place day after day are bound to attract attention, and the attention is likely to be closely followed by artillery fire or air raids. As well as offering physical cover, assembly areas should either be out of radar range, or masked by the terrain, and the entry and exit routes likewise.

The chosen assembly area must provide good cover and concealment not only for aircraft, but for the vehicles and equipment of the maintenance and re-supply crews.

Built-up areas are generally preferable to sites out in the countryside. Supermarkets, warehouses and factory sites all provide good hardstanding for the helicopters and metalled roads for the vehicles, as well as the sort of buildings that can be adapted for aircraft maintenance. The buildings can be blacked out at night so that maintenance work can continue round the clock.

The whole assembly area should be spread over as wide an area as possible – a company will need two or three square kilometres – to minimise the risk from artillery or air strikes.

An attack helicopter unit has a very small complement of men, and all of them have specific mission responsibilities. Wherever possible, local ground forces should provide security, and in any event the helicopter unit commander should be in very close touch with his counterpart on the ground.

On the ground, just as in the air, the attack helicopter unit is organised into teams along with the air scouts who fly with them. Ideally, the fighting units should be grouped around the perimeter of the assembly area with the operational command post at the centre.

Individual team members stay with their aircraft at all times with the exception of the unit leaders, who stay at the operations centre where they are immediately available.

BATTLE POSITIONS

To organise and control their movement to battle, attack helicopter units apply this standard system.

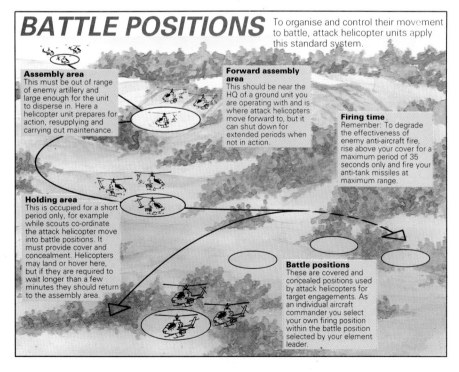

Assembly area
This must be out of range of enemy artillery and large enough for the unit to disperse in. Here a helicopter unit prepares for action, resupplying and carrying out maintenance.

Forward assembly area
This should be near the HQ of a ground unit you are operating with and is where attack helicopters move forward to, but it can shut down for extended periods when not in action.

Firing time
Remember: To degrade the effectiveness of enemy anti-aircraft fire, rise above your cover for a maximum period of 35 seconds only and fire your anti-tank missiles at maximum range.

Holding area
This is occupied for a short period only, for example while scouts co-ordinate the attack helicopter move into battle positions. It must provide cover and concealment. Helicopters may land or hover here, but if they are required to wait longer than a few minutes they should return to the assembly area.

Battle positions
These are covered and concealed positions used by attack helicopters for target engagements. As an individual aircraft commander you select your own firing position within the battle position selected by your element leader.

effective range of your offensive weapons is greater than that, then you've got him – but only if you do everything just right.

You may be involved in four main types of offensive operations:

1 Movement to contact
2 Hasty attack
3 Deliberate attack
4 Exploitation

These operations tend to follow on, one from another, but you have to keep flexible. At any stage you must be ready to back up and consolidate in the face of effective opposition, or skip a stage or two and turn a static situation into a running chase.

Movement to contact

Often, you may not know exactly where the enemy forces are situated. You can find them by sending out reconnaissance patrols, but often it's more effective to move a considerable force forward until contact is made – it's quicker, and you gain ground.

But because it involves rapid movement and decentralisation of command and control, it can lead to dis-

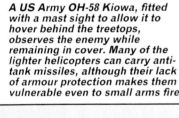

A US Army OH-58 Kiowa, fitted with a mast sight to allow it to hover behind the treetops, observes the enemy while remaining in cover. Many of the lighter helicopters can carry anti-tank missiles, although their lack of armour protection makes them vulnerable even to small arms fire.

organisation and reduce the attack force's ability to fight effectively unless communications function really well.

Communications hardware

One thing you can be sure of in a multi-million-pound attack helicopter is top quality communications hardware, and that's just one of the reasons why a helicopter force is often

The attack helicopter company commander must establish FARPs (Forward Arming and Refuelling Points) able to resupply five attacks and three scout helicopters simultaneously.

at the forefront of a movement-to-contact operation.

Find the enemy's weak spots. Use the best combination of friendly forces to mount the attack. Maintain security. Strike a balance between

control and aggression. Now move! Seizing the initiative early will give you the best chance of catching the enemy off balance.

When you do make contact with the enemy, the speed of the attack helicopter gives you the option of launching a hasty attack or reporting the position and bypassing, leaving it to be assaulted by other arms.

The decision will be based on the strategic value of the enemy detachment and on your own actual mission. You may find that your massive firepower means that you can take the target out on your way past. But don't get side-tracked into attacking a target of opportunity when your real objective is elsewhere – you always run the risk of upsetting a wider plan.

Hasty attack

A hasty attack is generally planned on the move, and carried out with a maximum of aggression and violence. Unit SOPs (Standard Operating Procedures) are of very high value when it comes to planning an attack – or a defensive action – when time is very short.

Instead of having to describe individual manoeuvres in detail, if they form part of the SOP you can refer to them just by name, and everyone will know what they have to do. The smaller the attack force, the more important it is to be properly drilled in the procedures.

You can often use a hasty attack to gauge the enemy's strength and will to resist, but it needs fine judgement on the part of the attack force commander to decide when to press home an assault that looks as though it might find itself in difficulties, in the hope of winning a quick victory, and when to re-group and plan the operation more carefully.

Deliberate attack

During the deliberate attack, the helicopter force will operate within strictly controlled limits as part of the combined arms team. The long-range anti-armour capability of the ATGMs (anti-tank guided missiles) is the most important part of your armoury, and so suppression of enemy armour will be your first task.

As soon as enemy tank activity is contained, then the attack helicopters are switched to other targets, to:
1 Attack and contain pockets of resistance bypassed by the main force.
2 Provide a fire base for advancing ground forces.
3 Dominate key terrain not yet under friendly control, to stop the enemy from mounting an effective counter-attack.
4 Destroy or repel any counter-attack the enemy is able to mount.

5 Attack withdrawing enemy forces or reserves.

Exploitation

Once you've hurt the enemy badly with an assault – or, better still, got him on the move – he must be prevented from re-grouping or conducting an orderly withdrawal.

The attack force will keep on at the

An AH-1 flies over a column of M113 APCs on exercise. When on the offensive, attack helicopters can fix the enemy and allow ground forces to manoeuvre and assault under covering fire.

enemy, advancing towards his rear areas where the command posts and supply stations will be located. Small pockets of resistance will be bypassed, but lightly defended installations should be destroyed in passing.

PICK OFF ENEMY ANTI-AIRCRAFT WEAPONS

Your primary target in an enemy mechanised or tank unit will be the ZSU-23-4 self-propelled radar controlled anti-aircraft guns. If you can eliminate these quickly, the rest of an enemy unit can be destroyed in relative safety. Their maximum range is 3000 metres and the maximum range of a TOW anti-tank missile is 3750 metres, so make sure you use this vital margin.

Use the 70-mm rockets against enemy armoured forces to compel them to close up. Once their hatches are shut, all tanks except the T-64 are unable to fire their anti-aircraft machine-guns and they will find it very hard to see you.

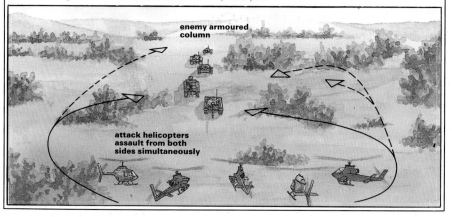

enemy armoured column

attack helicopters assault from both sides simultaneously

Helicopter Attack

Now one of the US Army's primary anti-tank weapon systems, the AH-64 Apache is the most powerful helicopter gunship in NATO. Swooping low across the battlefield, flying and fighting with an attack helicopter demands the skills of a tank crew and the quick reactions of a flier.

The gunner sits in front of the pilot and operates the gunship's weapons using a helmet-mounted sight. The crew compartment is armoured and will protect you even if the helicopter is shot down.

When the first attack helicopters poked their ugly, gun-loaded noses over the Vietnamese horizon in the early days of the war in South East Asia, the Viet Cong and NVA units they decimated could not have known that they were experiencing the first taste of a weapon that would change the face of battle. The early attack helicopters were known as helicopter gunships, which reflected the way in which they were armed and operated. Using modified infantry machine-guns mounted in the nose, in belly pods and in the open doorways, they went looking for detachments of enemy infantry in much the same way as a fast patrol boat would scout around for suitable targets.

All this changed with the development of light, accurate guided missiles capable of destroying Main Battle Tanks and other heavily-armoured vehicles and fortified ground posi-

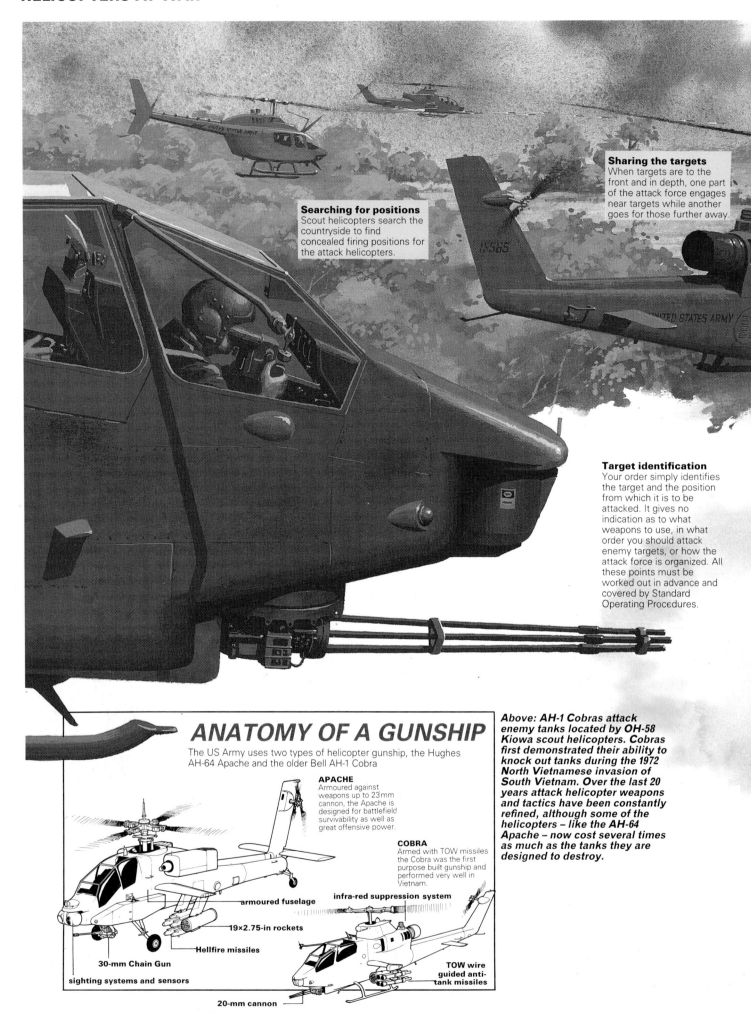

Searching for positions
Scout helicopters search the countryside to find concealed firing positions for the attack helicopters.

Sharing the targets
When targets are to the front and in depth, one part of the attack force engages near targets while another goes for those further away.

Target identification
Your order simply identifies the target and the position from which it is to be attacked. It gives no indication as to what weapons to use, in what order you should attack enemy targets, or how the attack force is organized. All these points must be worked out in advance and covered by Standard Operating Procedures.

ANATOMY OF A GUNSHIP

The US Army uses two types of helicopter gunship, the Hughes AH-64 Apache and the older Bell AH-1 Cobra

APACHE
Armoured against weapons up to 23mm cannon, the Apache is designed for battlefield survivability as well as great offensive power.

COBRA
Armed with TOW missiles the Cobra was the first purpose built gunship and performed very well in Vietnam.

armoured fuselage

infra-red suppression system

19×2.75-in rockets

Hellfire missiles

30-mm Chain Gun

sighting systems and sensors

20-mm cannon

TOW wire guided anti-tank missiles

Above: AH-1 Cobras attack enemy tanks located by OH-58 Kiowa scout helicopters. Cobras first demonstrated their ability to knock out tanks during the 1972 North Vietnamese invasion of South Vietnam. Over the last 20 years attack helicopter weapons and tactics have been constantly refined, although some of the helicopters – like the AH-64 Apache – now cost several times as much as the tanks they are designed to destroy.

HELICOPTER ATTACK

In combat you have little time to plan your attack and the distribution of your fire. This is the sort of engagement order you can expect: "Attack enemy forces in Engagement Area Bravo from Battle Positions Two, Three and Four."

Front and rear
When you attack an enemy column from both sides, the attack from the right goes against the rear of the enemy and shifts its fire towards the middle while the left flanking element starts from the front.

Target allocation
The attack element leader decides the weapons mix and the allocation of individual targets to individual helicopters, following your SOPs.

Long-range attack
Attack helicopters keep spread out but pointed towards the enemy forces. You attack from the longest range possible, making maximum use of cover and concealment.

Beyond enemy range
Long-range engagement may allow you to attack enemy tanks beyond the effective range of the ZSU 23-4 self-propelled anti-aircraft guns which accompany them.

Moving fire inwards
Modern anti-tank guided weapons whether laser- or wire-guided, cannot criss-cross the battlefield without getting their guidance systems hopelessly tangled. Outside elements of the attack force should engage outside elements of the enemy and move their fire inwards towards the enemy centre.

Right and left
When the attack is to come from one flank, the element on the left of your force attacks targets to its front and works towards the left of the enemy column. The right-hand element attacks the enemy to its front and then works to the right of the enemy column.

Target indication
Target indication is similar to that used by infantrymen: you use obvious terrain features as reference points and identify enemy units by their position relative to them. However, you must give a compass bearing from the reference point since helicopters could be approaching the target from any direction.

ATTACK PRIORITIES

Standard operational procedure (SOP) lays down two ways of deciding in which order targets are to be attacked: **Target Priority** and **Engagement Priority.**

Target Priority is the order in which different types of target are to be engaged:
1 Air defence artillery
2 Attack helicopters (if they are a direct threat)
3 Command tanks
4 Other tanks
5 Command and control vehicles
6 Anti-tank vehicles
7 Direct artillery fire
8 Mechanised troop carriers
9 Troop concentrations
The second method, **Engagement Priority**, is a sort of sub-group of the first set, depending on:
1 Immediate threat to yourself
2 Immediate threat to other platoon members
3 Immediate threat to other friendly forces
4 Other targets of opportunity

tions at ranges of a mile or more.

With the change of the helicopter's role from infantry hunter to tank killer, there came a profound change of tactics. Gone were the days of lone gunships going out on search-and-destroy missions. Instead, the helicopter pilot's job came more and more to resemble that of the tank commander – operating in teams, giving mutual support from covered positions, overwatching advances, hull-down concealment, and movement from place to place using every scrap of natural cover and protection.

All the operational manuals – and this section is taken from the US FM 17-50, Attack Helicopter Operations – stress the need for the aircraft to be used aggressively. 'Seize, retain and exploit the initiative', they tell you, time and time again until it's second nature.

These new tactics mean that you have to learn a new repertoire of low-level flying techniques. Contour following is the less terrifying of the two methods. Plotting a course in some-

The widespread use of attack helicopters dates from the Vietnam War when utility helicopters like this Bell UH-1 'Huey' were fitted with a variety of weapons. Here a door gunner fires twin .30-cal Browning machine-guns at Viet Cong positions in the Mekong Delta.

FIRING THE HELLFIRE

The Hellfire missile homes in on a tank 'illuminated' by a laser beam from another helicopter or a soldier on the ground. This enables you to strike at the enemy without them seeing you and taking defensive action.

3 The missile will home in on the target being illuminated by the laser beam, and you can pop back into cover.

2 You pop up from behind a clump of trees and fire a Hellfire missile.

4 So long as the scout helicopter can continue to point the laser at the tank, the missile will hit and blow it to pieces. The scout has not fired any weapons, so its position is not betrayed by any telltale flash.

1 A scout helicopter aims a laser beam at an enemy tank.

thing like a straight line, you adjust your altitude to keep a constant height above ground.

Hedge-hopping, it used to be called; but the fixed-wing pilots who coined that phrase in World War II would have a collective heart attack if they saw the lengths that modern attack helicopter pilots go to. You really do hop hedges – and trees, garden sheds and even low walls, so close to the ground do you fly.

Nap-of-the-earth

Even closer to the ragged edge is a technique called nap-of-the-earth (NOE). To fly NOE, you use the same ground-hugging manoeuvres as in straightforward contour-following flying, but you fly a meandering course that makes use of every scrap of cover – a country lane, for example, where there are hedges to hide the main body of the aircraft, the rotor blades skimming their tops. Or down the bed of a river wide enough for the tips of the blades to clear the trees on each side.

Helicopters such as the AH-1 Cobra and AH-64 Apache, along with the fixed-wing A-10 Thunderbolt II tank-buster, are the mainstay of US ground support operations. Masterpieces of technological sophistication, their computer-controlled Target Acquisition and Designation System/Pilot Night Vision Sensor (TADS/PNVS) allows the crew of pilot and gunner to find and lock onto targets in unbelievably bad visibility.

The weapons system, fully integrated into the TADS computer and capable of being operated by voice alone, is just as advanced. Fire-and-forget missiles, rockets, and the 30-mm quick-firing cannon combine

to give just one relatively small helicopter the sort of fire power that could previously only be amassed by a squadron of tanks.

And compared with other military aircraft of similar performance, the US attack helicopters *are* small – the overall length of the AH-1 is 13 metres, only two-thirds that of the Mi-24 'Hind', the Soviet Bloc's nearest equivalent. It's narrow too – because the pilot and gunner sit in tandem, the overall width can be kept down to just one metre across the cockpit: a very hard target to hit under battlefield conditions.

Even if you do receive incoming fire from ground forces, there's a good chance not only that you will survive, but also that you'll be able to continue with your mission. All the vulnerable parts of attack helicopters are fitted with titanium armour. Light in weight but very strong, this is capable of stopping small-arms fire of all types, including that from the 12.7-mm heavy machine-gun.

Finding the target

Scouting and reconnaissance are not carried out by the attack helicopter; it's not equipped for that purpose. This job is the province of small, fast, scout craft, fitted out to spot and mark targets for the attacking aircraft. When the scouting detachment has identified a target and made its report to the area commander, it performs a local holding action, co-ordinating whatever force is available in the area.

It also gathers local intelligence, ready to pass an accurate situation report to the attack helicopters when they arrive at the pre-designated holding area. This holding area will be just

minutes' flying time away from the target, but in a secure location that offers cover and concealment.

The attack and scout force commanders will use this information, constantly updated, to prepare a plan of action. To achieve surprise, the attack helicopter pilot uses all his skill and the flying aids at his command to get into an attack position unseen. By this stage the attack force will have split into two elements, in order to provide mutual 'fire and movement' protection.

Target position

As soon as you reach the attack position, you'll be notified of 'target handover' by the scout force commander, who has been responsible for the action until this point. Now you take your first quick look at the target, a procedure called 'partial unmasking'. This usually requires you to gain height until you can see over the tree-tops, record the scene in front of you with the TADS built-in video-recorder, and then return to concealment.

The sophisticated computer software then allows you to choose a target, unmask completely, acquire the chosen target, designate a weapons sub-system, and fire the weapon – all in less time than it takes for enemy anti-aircraft defences to line you up.

The first element of the attack force will fire two or three missiles in this way. The second element observes, looking especially carefully for anti-aircraft fire, which it will immediately suppress. Then the second element uses its main armament on any target still in action while the first element is changing position.

LYNX

TANK KILLER

Originally designed as a 12-seat light transport helicopter, the Lynx has been developed into one of the world's finest anti-armour missile platforms. The beautifully streamlined and light-weight fuselage and powerful Rolls-Royce Gem turboshaft engines make the Lynx one of the fastest helicopters over the battlefield – or anywhere. On 11 August 1986, the modified Lynx demonstrator set a new helicopter absolute speed record of 216.45 knots, although standard Army Lynxes usually cruise at 120 knots.

The killer elite

The Lynx combines its high speed with superb manoeuvrability, so that it can fly swiftly to the battle area while twisting and turning at ultra-low level to make maximum use of cover. Helicopter pilots call this flying 'nap-of-earth': their aim is always to be behind or in front of high ground or trees, not outlined against the sky.

A Westland Lynx utility helicopter moves across the desert in the short Saudi Arabian twilight. Lynxes went to the Gulf with the air element of Britain's 1st Armoured Division.

Lynx 'Helarm'

The Helarm (Helicopter armed action) is probably the single most effective method of halting an enemy armoured thrust. But how does the Lynx find its target and move into the firing position? A typical action might take place in West Germany.

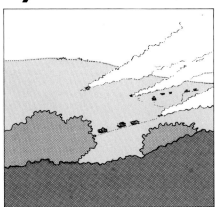

1 West Germany is superb anti-tank helicopter country, full of geographical features that channel enemy armour into predictable areas and easily-blockable 'choke points'.

2 If an enemy armoured division breaks through it will be found and kept under observation by a low-flying pair of Gazelle observation and reconnaissance helicopters.

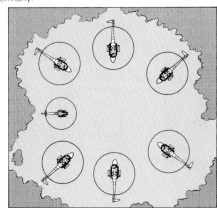

3 The Lynxes wait to be called forward at the 'holding RV', arranged in a circle to allow a good look-out to be maintained, with each Lynx covering the rear of the opposite aircraft.

Inside the Lynx

Roof-mounted sight
The TOW sight is built by British Aerospace Dynamics, and is based on a Hughes design. It is fitted with de-icing and demisting equipment, and has provision for laser rangefinding. Night/all-weather capability will be added later.

In any future conflict, the threat of NBC (Nuclear, Biological and Chemical) contamination would be severe; crew and passengers would routinely wear heavy and uncomfortable NBC protective clothing. The cabin is large and spacious, with canvas bench seats to accommodate up to nine soldiers. Troops would not usually be carried on a mission in which TOW missiles were used.

Aircrewman/gunner
The left-hand seat is occupied by the aircrewman, who acts as the gunner and assists the pilot with navigation and communications.

Pilot
The right-hand seat is occupied by the pilot/aircraft commander, whose hands are full just flying the Lynx!

Warhead
The Hughes TOW contains a shaped-charge HEAT (High Explosive Anti-Tank) warhead, capable of penetrating the thickest armour.

Control fins
Tail-mounted control fins and stabilising fins mounted amidships flick out as soon as the missile leaves its tube.

Guidance wires
Twin guidance wires transmit flightpath corrections to the missile from the gunner's joystick, via the SACLOS (Semi-Automatic Command to Line Of Sight) system.

Two further elements go to making Lynx such a formidable anti-tank weapon: its tremendous fire-power and the men who fly it.

The Lynx is operated by a two-man crew, consisting of a pilot/aircraft commander in the right-hand seat and an aircrewman/gunner in the left-hand seat. Most Army Air Corps aircrew are not commissioned, and the university-educated intellectual common in other areas of military aviation is something of a rarity in the Lynx force. These pilots and gunners tend to come from ordinary backgrounds, and are transformed into an elite fighting force by flair, dedication, *esprit de corps*, and a training that is second to none.

Tactics on the battlefield

The current philosophy is to use large numbers of helicopters as a Helarm (Helicopter armed action) to make a decisive attack on a division-sized enemy formation, gathering from previously surveyed ambush sites, known as Fire Positions, on pre-selected killing grounds. The Lynxes would usually be used as a commander's reserve, winning time for ground forces to redeploy or react in the face of an enemy thrust.

The key to success lies in the fact that the Lynx commander fights on ground of his own choosing, with good concealment, withdrawal routes and fields of fire. The tactics are to hit and run, falling back to other familiar fire positions to hit the enemy again. The Lynx can engage vastly more numerous enemy armoured forces with direct fire or by inserting anti-tank missile teams, and can act independently as well as in concert with armour, infantry, artillery or close air support.

4 Messages are passed on using small code cards which are read through the TOW sight, or by flashing the landing lights. Radio conversation, where necessary, is usually in code.

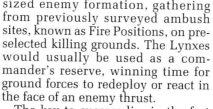
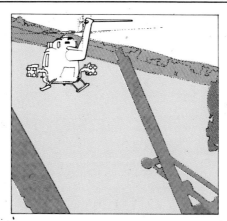

5 The group splits into two three-aircraft fire-teams and these fly 'nap-of-earth' to the fire position, keeping as low as possible to take full advantage of terrain masking.

6 The ideal fire position provides a screen of cover in front of the aircraft. From the front only the rotors and roof mounted sight should be visible, except when the Lynx pops up to fire.

Rotor
The Lynx's semi-rigid titanium rotor head is uniquely strong and flexible, and allows unparalleled manoeuvrability.

Cabin
The Lynx can accommodate nine fully-armed troops in its capacious cabin, with two crew members in the cockpit.

Engines
The Lynx is powered by two Rolls-Royce Gem turboshaft engines, mounted side-by-side on top of the upper fuselage decking.

TOW tubes
The Lynx AH.Mk 1 carries four TOW missile launch tubes on each side of the fuselage. Reloads can be carried in the cabin, but this is not usual.

Request for action

A request for a Lynx Helarm can come directly from a ground unit, or more usually from an obs and recce (observation and reconnaissance) pair of Gazelles. These two helicopters fly nap-of-earth, looking for and keeping track of the enemy while staying just out of range of the MBT (Main Battle Tank) armament, anti-aircraft artillery and small arms fire. They report back to the Helarm commander in the lead Lynx, and to the Helarm director in a third Gazelle.

During hostilities, a Lynx squadron would operate from a temporary HLS (Helicopter Landing Site), which would itself move as often as twice a day. Sometimes an HLS would be set up in woodland: support vehicles and tents will hide in the trees, and the helicopters will park on the edge of an adjacent field, covered by camouflage netting. More often, an urban site would be used, with the helicopters parked in a supermarket or filling station, since buildings give better concealment and protection against NBC (Nuclear, Biological and Chemical) weapons and blast. All personnel would work in full NBC protective clothing, and would rest in a 'Porton liner', an inflatable tent with 'clean' air and a system of air-locks, or in a

7 The gunner of the Lynx selects a target from the sector assigned to his helicopter, and uses a small joystick to position the sight cross-hairs over it.

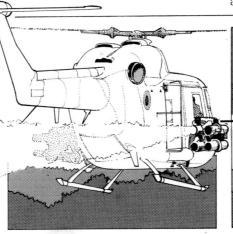

8 The gunner grasps the trigger in his right hand and the joystick in his right hand. He has already selected which TOW he wishes to fire, and does so when the Lynx pops up above its cover.

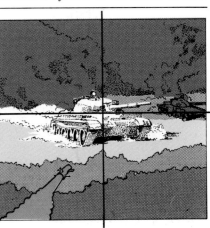

9 The sight of the TOW missile automatically tracks the weapon, and steers it to the target centred in the cross-hairs.

vehicle-mounted 'protection unit', based on a four-ton box body.

Out of hiding . . .

When action is imminent, the Lynx squadron goes to 15 minutes' standby. While the pilots take the camouflage off their aircraft, or get them into the open, the crewmen are briefed in the Squadron Command Post (CP). The aircraft then fly to the 'holding RV' (holding rendezvous), a safe field or clearing within a few minutes' flight of the selected fire position. The aircraft wait, sometimes with one engine shut down to conserve fuel, until called forward by the Helarm director in a Gazelle. The Lynxes sit in a wide circle, pointing inwards to allow code-cards held up by the Helarm commander to be read by the other crewmen through their TOW sights. This arrangement also allows a full 360 degree lookout against enemy aircraft or troops, with each crew looking beyond the helicopter opposite them in the circle.

Flying from the holding RV to a final RV or directly to the fire position, the pilot makes the maximum use of cover, sacrificing speed for an unseen approach, hover-taxiing very low, often into a fire position familiar from peacetime exercises. Sometimes a fire position will be in front of a line of trees, against which the black and green Lynx will hardly be visible or, more often, behind trees or a ridge. If behind cover the Lynx will expose only its rotors and roof-mounted sight for the aircrewman to get on a target,

The Lynx AH.Mk 7 is a developed version of the helicopter. It can be heavily armed with Hellfire missiles and cannon.

popping up briefly to fire, and then slipping back.

. . . into the firing line

The squadron's six Lynxes would usually have split into two fire teams of three at the final RV, either going forward to two separate fire positions, or using the same fire position in a relay. The leader of each fire team usually flies the middle aircraft at the fire position, and is responsible for destroying close and mid-range targets, in that order. The outer aircraft concentrates on the flanks, on extreme-range targets. When all missiles have been fired, or if forced back by enemy fire, the fire team would withdraw to the flank.

When operating with fixed-wing support aircraft against an enemy column, the Lynx would concentrate on enemy anti-aircraft artillery vehicles, leaving the tanks to USAF A-10 Thunderbolts or RAF Harriers.

Lynx saw its anti-armour combat debut in the Persian Gulf in 1991. The war itself was unusual: flat desert terrain with little or no vegetation meant that there were few of the hiding places that pilots in Central Europe are taught to use. By the same token, however, you could see enemy troop positions relatively easily, and if the enemy was on the move then the desert sand that was kicked up meant that you could see a vehicle at great distances. The long sight lines meant that your own weapons could be used out to the limits of their range.

This Lynx belongs to the Army Air Corps. The helicopter can operate independently, or in conjunction with other Army units or close-support aircraft.

LYNX HAS.Mk 3

The naval Lynx is the wheeled variant of a multi-role helicopter also serving the army on skids.
Light alloy is used for primary structure in the semi-monocoque pod and boom of this helicopter, with glass fibre employed for various components such as fairings and access doors. Two crew members sit side-by-side: pilot to starboard and navigator (with his radar display) to port. There is no bulkhead behind the crew, which allows easy access to the cabin. A semi-rigid main rotor was chosen for the Lynx, the blades being constructed from glass-reinforced plastics over a Nomex core. Manual rearward folding of the blades and forward folding of the fin facilitate storage in confined spaces.

Height restriction

Naval requirements also specified a height restriction for the Lynx, with the result that the engines and gear-box are mounted neatly above the cabin and there is no visible rotor spindle. Westland produced a compact, reliable gear-box to reduce the engine speed of 6,150 rpm to 326 rpm for the main rotor, while Rolls-Royce exercised similar care in the design of the Gem turboshaft.

Operating the Lynx from stern platforms requires special techniques. Projecting from the bottom of the cabin is a hydraulically-powered deck-lock, the jaws of which grasp a metal lattice set onto the deck. The single main (rear) wheels are splayed outwards and the twin nose-wheel

The Westland Lynx is one of the most successful naval helicopters currently in service. During the Gulf War Royal Navy Lynx helicopters destroyed most of the Iraqi patrol boat flotilla operating along the Kuwaiti coastline.

The Lynx can be equipped either for anti-submarine warfare or to engage surface vessels with its Sea Skua missiles, as seen here. The Lynx can also be used to decoy incoming missiles away from its parent ship.

unit is set at right angles to the fuse-lage axis. These allow the helicopter to pivot into wind on its swivelling deck-lock, without the parent vessel having to change course. With engines running at take-off power, the Lynx releases its lock and leaps into the air, so obviating the dangers of a more leisurely departure from a pitching and heaving deck.

Landing is undertaken with the main wheels splayed outwards at 27 degrees and the nose wheel set forward to prevent pivoting. Judging the appropriate moment, the pilot lands firmly on the deck, knowing that the landing gear can absorb descent rates of up to 2.3 metres per second. By changing the main rotor blade pitch, he can employ up to 1361 kilograms of reverse thrust to pin the Lynx to the deck until he is certain that the lock is firmly holding the grille. As a further safety measure, the helicopter is fitted with sprag brakes: the type has a ratchet instead of pads, and so can only be set either fully on or fully off.

On the assumption that a warplane is only as good as its operational equipment, the Lynx must be reckoned a very capable helicopter. It benefits from several new, advanced

HMS Birmingham's Lynx on a wildly moving flight deck. Operating from a frigate, a helicopter is more affected by the sea state than those aboard aircraft or helicopter carriers.

systems, including the Ferranti ARI 5979 Seaspray radar, which is able to detect and track the type of small, high-speed attack craft whose missiles pose an increasing menace to major warships. Operating in the I-band, Seaspray employs frequency agility for improved performance in high sea states and in the face of jamming, and may also be used for general maritime surveillance or the pro-

vision of over-the-horizon targeting facilities for the anti-ship missiles of allied vessels. The Seaspray scanner is located inside a completely removable radome which forms the Lynx's nose, and its findings are displayed on a bright TV screen tabulated with data, including a readout of target range and bearing.

A prime function of Seaspray is target illumination for the BAe Sea Skua

during the Falklands war, some of it at night with the aid of pilot's thermal imaging equipment.

The first 60 RN Lynx helicopters were to HAS.Mk 2 standard with Gem 2 engines, while the balance, issued to units from June 1982 onwards, are HAS.Mk 3s employing the uprated Gem 41-1. From 1987 HAS.Mk 3s were retrofitted with a Racal central tactical system that processes all sensor equipment and presents mission information on a single multi-function screen. Similar engine improvements are to be found in the two versions of the Lynx delivered to France's naval air arm, the Aéronavale, designated HAS.Mk 2(FN) and HAS.Mk 4(FN).

Built at Yeovil between 1977 and 1983, the 40 French helicopters were little more than flying shells when de-

Above: The Argentine supply ship Rio Carcarana burns off the Falklands after an attack by Royal Navy Lynx helicopters (right) armed with Sea Skua anti-ship missiles, 17 May 1982. Sea Skuas were rushed into service just in time for the war and proved very successful.

anti-ship missile. Being comparatively light, at 145 kilograms each, four of these weapons may be carried on outrigger pylons on the lower side of the cabin (only two missiles if the Lynx is to patrol well away from its vessel), and each has a range of at least 15 kilometres. After release, the Sea Skua progressively descends to a level pre-set according to the wave height at the time, then homes on reflected radar energy from the Seaspray until it strikes the target. The Lynx must slow down to fire Sea Skua and then remain in the area to provide illumination, but it is free to manoeuvre within reasonable bounds for its own safety. Premature service entry was achieved by the missile when development rounds were issued for operational use in the 1982 Falklands war. The score was four out of four.

Homing torpedoes

Similarly, pre-production Marconi Stingray homing torpedoes were assigned to the Lynx in April 1982 as a replacement for the usual Aerojet Mk 46s. The torpedo is carried as an alternative to missiles or BAe Type 11 Mod 3 depth charges. A further hasty addition for the South Atlantic conflict concerned a general-purpose machine-gun, mounted in either of the cabin doorways on a 'home-made' pintle, which was first used in combat against small Argentine ships at night. Some Lynx helicopters were fitted with equipment which would decoy Argentine Exocet sea-skimming missiles away from their targets, an occupation not as dangerous as it might first appear as long as the helicopter remained above the maximum height permitted by the missile's autopilot (about 60 metres).

Also boosted during 1982 were programmes of retrospective installation for ESM and MAD equipment. The former is a Racal MIR-2 'Orange Crop', the forward sensors for which are mounted prominently on the nose, to provide the bearing of enemy radar and radio transmissions. MIR-2 was the subject of an operational trial by the RN Lynx before widespread adoption, as was Texas Instruments ASQ-81 MAD. The towed 'bird' for the MAD equipment is installed in an attachment to the starboard main landing gear leg, and the first deployment was made experimentally in August 1981.

Falklands campaign

In all, Lynx helicopters flew 1,728 sorties (generating 2,567 airborne hours and 3,796 deck landings)

livered. Before issue to the service they were fitted with a French avionics suite, comprising Omera-Segid ORB-31-W radar and Alcatel DUAV-4 'dunking' sonar, plus local radios and other equipment. The ORB-31-W uses two transmitter/receivers (one for long distances and the other with greater sensitivity and clutter resistance), but French Lynx helicopters are armed only with up to four Aérospatiale AS.12 wire-guided missiles (range 6000 metres) and the associated SFIM APX M335 gyro-stabilised sight mounted in the roof above the port seat. Aéronavale Lynxes are operated from the aircraft carriers *Clemenceau* and *Foch*, the helicopter carrier *Jeanne d'Arc*, and C70 and F67 class destroyers.

The Netherlands operates two variants, mainly from 'Van Speijk'

Right: The Lynx serves aboard ships of the German, Dutch, French and Brazilian navies with different sensor fits and armament.

and 'Kortenaer' class frigates. These are the locally-designated SH-14B and SH-14C models, equipped, respectively, with French Alcatel DUAV-4 'dunking' sonar and ASQ-81 MAD. As with other Lynx models, Decca TANS is used for accurate navigation at sea, and an autohover mode on the Marconi AFCS provides vertical provision for dipping the sonar. West Germany's Bundesmarine introduced a further

variation on the theme by equipping its Lynx Mk 88s with Bendix AQS-18 sonar, again deployed from a central well by means of a hydraulic winch. They operate in pairs from the Type 122 or 'Bremen' class frigates.

Farther afield, Lynx helicopters are employed for the ASW/ASV role in South America and Africa. Argentina received two in 1978 for her British-built Type 42 destroyers *Hercules* and *Santisima Trinidad*, but one was lost in an accident at sea during the 1982 Falklands war and the other placed in storage when spares supplies were stopped. The first of a repeat order for eight Argentine Lynxes made its first flight two days before Argentine forces invaded the Falklands, so it was embargoed and used as a company demonstrator. Also in 1978, Brazil re-

ceived nine Lynx helicopters for its British-designed 'Noteroi' class frigates. Finally, the Nigerian navy's newly-formed air component received three Lynxes in 1984.

Surveillance models

Completing the Lynx picture, three more marks of the aircraft operate in Europe in surveillance and utility roles, rather than with ASW/ASV as their primary task. Apart from the Netherlands' UH-14As, which are assigned to SAR and light transport support of the marines, these helicopters have unusual lines of administration. Those operated from 'Hvidbjornen' class fishery patrol ves-

sels of the Danish navy belong to that service, yet are attached to No. 722 Squadron of the air force for maintenance and support. Norway's air arm flies Lynx helicopters in its No. 337 Squadron, and the helicopters wear the marking *Kystvakt* (Coast Guard) to indicate their operating agency and role of fishery protection, oil rig security and SAR. From its broad range of assignments, it can be seen that the Lynx combines many of the attributes of a large helicopter within a small package, and so can be judged an invaluable component of NATO's naval forces.

Having detected a submarine with its dipping sonar or sonobuoys, the Lynx can attack with Stingray torpedoes. Stingray homes in on the target submarine using its own onboard sonar.

SEA SKUA

The Sea Skua is a light air-to-surface missile carried by Royal Navy Lynx helicopters. Fitted with a 20-kilogram warhead, it is semi-active radar homing, so the helicopter must 'paint' the target with its radar to guide the missile onto its target.

The missile age at sea began in 1967. An Egyptian 'Komar' fast attack craft sank an Israeli destroyer with a pair of Soviet-built SS-N-2 'Styx' anti-ship missiles. It was a clear signal that even the smallest of warships now possessed considerable fighting power.

From those early days, the anti-ship missile was hailed as the means by which small navies could challenge much larger fleets for dominance of limited stretches of coastal water. However, such thoughts were premature, since the larger navies can generally afford larger, faster, more accurate missiles, and they can deploy them in much greater numbers.

One of the most successful missiles in recent years proved that point during the Gulf War. Iraq had a number of small missile-armed craft with which to threaten the coalition naval forces operating in the northern Gulf. With the occupation of Kuwait they also had access to the latest Western-designed craft armed with Exocet missiles.

Iraqi missile boats were less than successful, however. They had no answer to coalition air power, and above all they had no answer to the Sea Skua missile.

The British Aerospace Sea Skua is a lightweight weapon which arms helicopters of the Royal Navy. Carried by Lynxes operating from the decks of British destroyers and frigates, Sea Skua proved devastating against Iraq's fast attack craft. The Lynx-Sea Skua combination was one of the most effective naval weapons of the whole conflict. Twenty Sea Skuas were launched, sinking or seriously damaging 13 Iraqi fast attack craft and military vessels.

Design of the Sea Skua began in the

The Sea Skua was rushed into service at the time of the Falklands war and was used against several Argentine surface vessels off the islands.

1970s, with a requirement for a new-generation helicopter-launched anti-ship missile intended to engage small, fast-moving and agile surface targets. The first fully-guided trials took place in December 1979, and although it had not been declared fully operational, Sea Skua was deployed to the South Atlantic during the Falklands war. Eight missiles were fired, scoring eight hits; two Argentine vessels were sunk and two were damaged.

Semi-active radar-homing

Sea Skua is a semi-active radar-homing missile. The target is illuminated by the helicopter's frequency agile surveillance and target tracking radar, and the missile's seeker head homes in on the radar reflections from the target.

The missile is treated like a round of ammunition and needs little or no preparation before use. Sea Skua is powered by solid-propellant boost and sustainer motors, which ignite simultaneously upon being launched from the carrier helicopter. Its cruise height can be pre-set to one of four sea-skimming altitudes, depending on the sea state.

Once the missile has been launched, Sea Skua maintains its correct altitude by using a radio altimeter, maintaining course and height by means of cruciform canard control fins. It is controlled by an autopilot at this stage. Once near the position of the target a command instruction from the launch platform or from its own autopilot orders the missile to climb. This gives Sea Skua's radar-homing head a chance to lock on.

Sea Skua is fitted with a 20-kilogram high-explosive semi-armour-piercing warhead. In combat, this has proved quite effective at penetrating the hull and superstructure of a variety of targets of widely differing sizes.

Specification
Sea Skua

Dimensions: length 2.5 m; diameter 25 cm, span 72 cm
Propulsion: solid-propellant booster and sustainer
Performance: maximum speed Mach 0.9+; maximum range up to 25 km depending upon aircraft speed at launch
Guidance: semi-active radar homing
Warhead: 20-kg HE semi-armour piercing

Below: A Lynx launches a Sea Skua. Inset: Taking a break during the Falklands war. In the South Atlantic and the Gulf the Sea Skua has proved highly successful.

GAZELLE
EYES OVER THE BATTLEFIELD

A Royal Marines Gazelle AH.Mk 1 in its new colour scheme lands on the deck of a Royal Navy warship, somewhere off the coast of Norway.

A French army Gazelle looses off a Euromissile HOT wire-guided anti-tank missile. The Gazelle/HOT combination was used by both sides during the Gulf War.

Obs and Recce Mission

1 After a comprehensive briefing at squadron level, covering the task to be flown and the intelligence situation, frequencies, tactics and codes to be used, the crews of the Obs and Recce pair pre-flight their aircraft.

2 Where possible the aircrew will have a face-to-face briefing with the user, ascertaining exactly what they will be looking for and where, and where a Helarm would be most effective in stopping the enemy

3 The pair of aircraft will fly nap-of-earth, sacrificing speed in order to stay as low as possible. Maximum use is made of the terrain, and the aircraft fly below power lines to avoid 'skylining' themselves.

HELICOPTERS AT WAR

The Anglo-French Gazelle helicopter is an ideal scout: fast, highly manoeuvrable and relatively simple to maintain, even in the field. Some military Gazelles carry a wide variety of weapons: many French army ones are used in the anti-tank role, armed with Euromissile HOT optically-guided, tube-launched wire-guided anti-tank missiles.

Similarly armed anti-armour Gazelles are also used by Iraq, Kuwait, Morocco, Syria and Yugoslavia. Gazelles were used by both sides in the Gulf War, and Syrian aircraft saw action against the Israelis in the Lebanon in 1982. Some Yugoslav Gazelles also operate in the armed role, carrying two pairs of Soviet 'Sagger' (AT-3) missiles. Machine-guns and rockets are more likely to have been used recently, as the Yugoslav army fights against Croatian nationalists.

These aircraft are all fitted with modern roof-mounted sights for targeting the enemy, and their small size and high speed make them deadly adversaries on the battlefield.

The Gazelle is in service in large numbers with the British armed forces, being the standard basic training helicopter of all three services.

In time of war, some RAF training Gazelles would receive a hasty coat of camouflage paint and would be deployed to the battle area to be used to survey damage to airfields, and as liaison aircraft, shuttling back and forth to the dispersed sites used by the Harrier force.

Front-line use

The main British military operator of the Gazelle is the Army Air Corps, which uses the aircraft for training and as a front-line aircraft. Some of the AAC Gazelles sent 'Down South'

Ferranti/Avimo AF532 Gazelle Observation Aid
The Gazelle Observation Aid, as presently fitted to Army Air Corps aircraft, is not fitted with laser designating or rangefinding equipment, although this may be incorporated at a later date. The sight is roof-mounted, so can be used with the helicopter hovering behind cover.

Aircrewman
The left-hand seat of Army Air Corps helicopters is occupied by a non-commissoned aircrewman.

VHF/FM homing aerials

Pilot
The handling pilot sits in the right-hand seat and is traditionally the aircraft commander. The Army Air Corps is presently rethinking its crewing policies, so that the aircraft commander, a trained pilot, will sit in the left-hand seat, controlling the weapons systems, while a junior pilot will occupy the right-hand seat, actually flying the aircraft.

Armoured seats
Gazelles serving with the British Army of the Rhine are being fitted with armoured seats for increased crew protection. The Gazelle's vulnerability to ground fire was dramatically illustrated during the Falklands war.

Simple skid-type undercarriage.

4 The two aircraft remain some distance apart, one moving while the other is in contact. When in contact the Gazelle will remain just within sight of the enemy, but well outside the range of his guns.

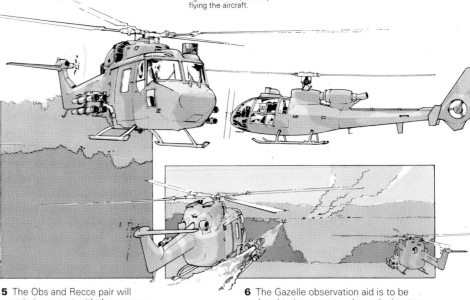

5 The Obs and Recce pair will remain in contact with the enemy at all times, and will guide the Lynx Helarm fire teams into position. The crewman will search for and identify targets using the roof-mounted observation aid.

6 The Gazelle observation aid is to be updated to incorporate a laser designator and a laser rangefinder, giving enhanced capability for the direction of Lynx/TOW Helarm missions.

Inside the Gazelle

Rotating anti-collision beacon

This Westland-built Gazelle AH.Mk 1 of the Army Air Corps is configured for an operational observation and reconnaissance sortie, with the crew wearing full NBC protective clothing. The pylon on the fuselage side carries a reconnaissance pod but could be used to mount other stores, including the Nitesun searchlight.

Fenestron tail rotor

UHF radio aerial
The UHF radio is used for longer range communications, and for military air-to-air radio traffic. Messages would seldom be passed in 'clear', a simple Batco (Battlefield Code) being used to enhance security.

VHF radio aerial
The VHF radio is used for communicating with ground forces using the Clansman radio, and certain types of single-channel set

Canadair reconnaissance pod
This streamlined pod contains a battery of Leica (Canada) optical cameras, for use in the photographic reconnaissance role. Limited all-weather capability is available by using infra-red film.

during the Falklands war in 1982 were armed with pintle-mounted GPMGs and SNEB unguided rocket launchers, but this weapons fit proved ineffective except as a morale-booster.

Twelve front-line Army Air Corps anti-tank squadrons are each equipped with one flight of TOW-armed Lynxes, and a flight of Gazelles. The Army Air Corps dedicated out-of-area rapid response unit, No. 658 Squadron, has used a mix of Gazelles and Westland Scouts, while the Royal Marines' own helicopter unit, No. 3 Commando Brigade Air Squadron, is equipped with Lynxes and Gazelles.

Several front-line Army Air Corps units are equipped with Gazelles only, fulfilling a wide variety of roles. The four Gazelles of No. 25 Flight, based in Belize, support the British Army and the Belize Defence Force in their efforts to protect the sovereignty of this tiny Commonwealth State

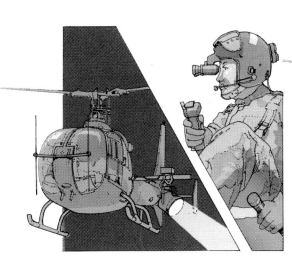

7 The Gazelle has a limited night capability, since the pilot and crewman can wear NVGs (Night Vision Goggles), which can be used with the roof-mounted observation aid. Some peacetime missions are mounted using the powerful Nitesun searchlight.

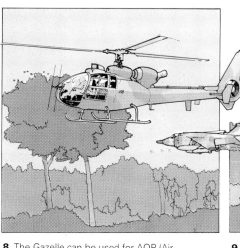

8 The Gazelle can be used for AOP (Air Observation Post) duties, spotting for artillery, or for FAC (Forward Air Control) work, guiding fixed wing close-support aircraft onto their targets.

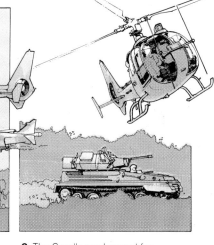

9 The Gazelle can be used for dedicated reconnaissance duties, equipped with a camera pod and working in conjunction with ground-based 'screen' reconnaissance units equipped with the Scorpion and Scimitar.

Above: The French army SA 341F Gazelle is armed with a 20-mm GIAT M.621 cannon on the starboard side. The weapon is light and virtually without recoil, making it an ideal helicopter weapon.

Right: The Gazelles of No. 25 Flight tend to follow roads or rivers, to minimise the dangers in the event of an engine failure. These single-engined choppers routinely fly over the impenetrable Belizean jungle, where a forced landing would usually be impossible.

against aggression by neighbouring Guatemala.

No. 7 Flight used to be based at RAF Gatow, East Berlin, and its three aircraft, prominently marked with a large Union Jack, were used to survey the Berlin Wall, to assist the local police, customs and fire service, and to act as liaison aircraft for the Berlin Brigade.

Northern Ireland base

Two of the Army's joint Gazelle/Lynx units are based in Northern Ireland, and are manned by aircrew from German-based squadrons. The squadrons do not have a Helarm (helicopter armed actions) commitment, so both Lynx and Gazelle are used for communications, transport and special duties. Both helicopter types can be used for the insertion of patrols, although night insertions are usually handled by the Lynx and by RAF Pumas and Wessexes.

Night searching

The Gazelle is sometimes used for night observation duties using the Nitesun searchlight, lighting up incidents or riots, with the Nitesun providing a variable area circle of total daylight.

The main use of the Gazelle is as an observation and reconnaissance tool supporting Lynx Helarms in armoured battle. During a typical Lynx Helarm mission, between 18 and 20 Lynxes will be committed, operating in fire teams of three and controlled by a Helarm Director. The Helarm Director will usually be the

second-in-command of the squadron or the Gazelle Flight Commander, and will fly in the left-hand seat of a Gazelle, directing the Lynxes into their fire positions and acting as a radio relay aircraft between the Helarm Commander in the lead Lynx and the Brigade HQ.

Two Gazelles will be used as an 'Obs and Recce' pair for forward reconnaissance. The aircraft would 'leapfrog' up to the engagement area, flying tactically to avoid detection and yet keeping the enemy and one another in sight at all times. In these circumstances the Gazelles may be vulnerable to small arms fire from enemy advanced reconnaissance parties and to enemy helicopters and fighter bombers operating ahead of the armoured thrust. Only the most experienced and disciplined aircrew will be chosen to fly the 'Obs and Recce' Gazelles, and the pilots will use nap-of-earth (NOE) techniques, staying as low as possible and making maximum use of the terrain to stay out of sight of the enemy.

Up-to-date info

Even though the whole of the potential battlefield has been pre-surveyed for suitable Helarm fire positions, the Gazelles will play a crucial role in gaining an up-to-date picture of enemy tank concentrations and dispositions, allowing the most effective use to be made of the Helarm. They will also be required to assess the most suitable new fire positions after the Lynxes have fired their first salvos of TOW missiles.

Where possible the helicopters will stay between three and four kilometres from the enemy, to stay outside the range of anti-aircraft artillery. They will never approach closer than 2000 metres, which is the effective range of a Main Battle Tank's gun.

The crews of the reconnaissance Gazelles have a variety of sophisticated modern aids to reduce the cockpit workload to manageable levels. The aircrewmen look at the target through the roof-mounted Ferranti AF532 Gazelle Observation Aid, which is a gyro-stabilised optical sight with magnification ratios of ×2.5 and ×10. It might in the future be updated with a laser target marker and laser rangefinder to give enhanced capability for directing Helarm operations.

Computer aids

The Gazelle is fitted with a Racal Decca TANS (Tactical Air Navigation System), a highly accurate Doppler-driven navigation aid which is invaluable during nap-of-earth operations. The CAP Scientific MIC (Mission Information Computer), a hand-held, high-power calculator, is used for solving mission management problems, including the decoding of messages.

Although the unarmed Gazelle lacks some of the glamour of the TOW missile-toting Lynx, it is every bit as important, acting as the eyes and ears of any Helarm operation. The Gazelle is fast, strong and manoeuvrable, well suited to tactical low-flying and giving its crew a remarkable field of view through its huge 'bubble' cockpit.

Specification

AGM-114 Hellfire

Type: helicopter-launched air-to-surface missile
Dimensions: length 1.63 m; body diameter 0.178 m; span 0.33 m
Launch weight: 46 kg
Propulsion: solid propellant rocket
Performance: speed supersonic; range 8 km
Warhead: 8-kg high-explosive shaped-charge

HELLFIRE!

The Hughes TOW wire-guided missile was very successful, giving helicopters unprecedented anti-armour capability. Even as it entered service, however, it was clear that improvements to air defence systems would make helicopters vulnerable. Wire-guided missiles have to be directed by hovering or slow-moving helicopters, and as surface-to-air missiles increased their range, such tactics became increasingly risky. Clearly something faster and longer-ranged would be necessary.

Development of the AGM-114 Hellfire began in 1972. The name is derived from an acronym, HELicopter-Launched FIRE-and-forget. The idea was for a missile that could be launched from a safe distance, continuing independently so that the attacking helicopter could immediately head for safety.

Hellfire entered service in 1985, increasing the US Army's anti-tank capability. The missile is semi-active laser-guided, a sensitive seeker in the nose homing the missile on the 'splash' of a coded laser beam reflecting off the target.

Designation can be by launch helicopter, in which case it must be able to see the target to keep the laser in position, or it can be provided by a third

An Apache makes one of the early trial firings of Hellfire. The fire-and-forget, laser-guided Hellfire is much more capable than previous wire-guided missiles like TOW or HOT.

party, usually a ground observer or another laser-equipped helicopter. This enables the attacking helicopter to 'fire-and-forget', getting clear as soon as the missile leaves its launch rail.

Shaped-charge warhead

Hellfire weighs 46 kilograms, with an eight kilogram shaped-charge warhead that can destroy most known tank armour. Defensive technology is always advancing, however, so Hell-

fire has to keep pace. It has been trialled with a tandem warhead in order to defeat reactive armour, and various guidance systems have been developed. These include imaging infra-red seeking and active radar-homing versions.

Hellfire is currently in service with the US Army and the US Marine Corps, as well as with Sweden where it is used as a coast defence weapon. Its major combat debut came in the Gulf War, when US Army AH-64 Apaches armed with Hellfire proved to be probably the most effective tank killers of the war, reaping a grim harvest amongst Iraq's army.

US Army ground crewmen load Hellfires onto an AH-64 Apache's port inboard station. Apaches can carry up to 16 of the hard-hitting Hellfires, but a more normal weapon load is eight missiles on the helicopter's inner pylons with 19-round air-to-ground rocket pods on the outer pylons.

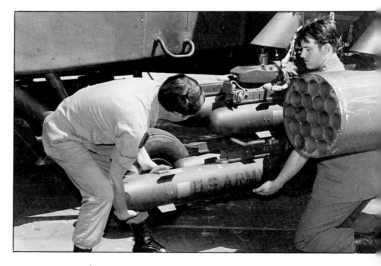

Engagement sequence

1 Detection

Modern attack helicopters are equipped with a variety of sensors that enable them to engage targets by day or night, through the fire and smoke of the battlefield. Hellfire's main platform is the amazing McDonnell AH-64 Apache. This is equipped with a sophisticated Target Acquisition and Designation System/Pilot's Night Vision System (TADS/PNVS). TADS combines a TV camera and a direct vision system with a laser rangefinder/designator, a laser spot tracker and a forward-looking infra-red sight. The PNVS is a forward-looking infra-red sensor that displays its imagery via the integrated helmet and display sighting system onto a monocle in front of one of the pilot's eyes.

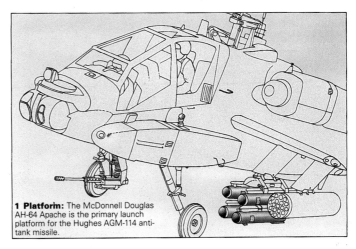

1 Platform: The McDonnell Douglas AH-64 Apache is the primary launch platform for the Hughes AGM-114 anti-tank missile.

2 Designation

Laser-guidance has brought about a revolution in the accuracy of air-to-ground weapons. The principle is simple: an infra-red laser beam, invisible to the naked eye, is directed onto a target. Reflections from that beam are detected by an attacking aircraft or missile, and the sensor in the nose of the missile homes in to make the kill. Hellfire is usually carried by Apache attack helicopters, which are equipped with lasers to do their own designating. In high threat environments, however, the designation can be provided by a third party: either a forward observer, or a scout helicopter with a mast-mounted sight that can designate from behind cover.

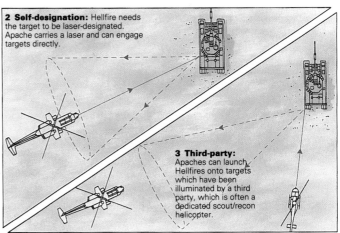

2 Self-designation: Hellfire needs the target to be laser-designated. Apache carries a laser and can engage targets directly.

3 Third-party: Apaches can launch Hellfires onto targets which have been illuminated by a third party, which is often a dedicated scout/recon helicopter.

3 Engagement

In direct fire, Hellfire can be launched from an Apache as long as it can see the target and can keep the laser designator in position. With third-party designation, blind shots can be made. The missile is launched from low level before its seeker has locked onto the laser spot. It will search for the reflected laser beam and then lock on to make the attack. Coding the laser designator, using different wavelengths or pulses of laser energy, enables the attacking aircraft to ripple-fire as many missiles as there are designators. Each missile will home in on only the reflection it is coded for, enabling one helicopter to attack several targets simultaneously.

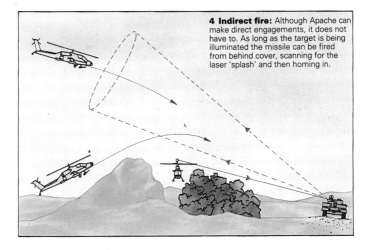

4 Indirect fire: Although Apache can make direct engagements, it does not have to. As long as the target is being illuminated the missile can be fired from behind cover, scanning for the laser 'splash' and then homing in.

4 Target destroyed

Shaped-charged warheads like that carried by Hellfire use a jet of liquid metal blasted forwards explosively to smash through enemy armour plate. If that jet can be disrupted, then the shaped-charge has little effect. Reactive armour has just that effect, exploding outwards when hit and so disrupting the incoming warhead. Hellfire has been tested with a tandem warhead. The first charge detonates, exploding the reactive armour on the enemy vehicle and being disrupted in the process. A split second later, the second charge goes off, but as the reactive armour has already exploded, there is nothing to disrupt the jet of liquid metal, which breaks through the armour into the interior of the tank.

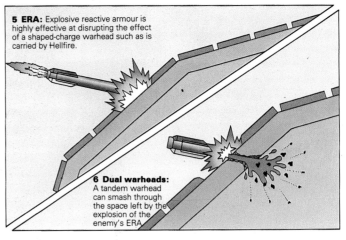

5 ERA: Explosive reactive armour is highly effective at disrupting the effect of a shaped-charge warhead such as is carried by Hellfire.

6 Dual warheads: A tandem warhead can smash through the space left by the explosion of the enemy's ERA.

AIR MOBILE WITH THE HUEY

A UH-1 'Huey' of the US Army heads west into the sunset across the Mekong Delta. It was the Huey which made possible the new air-mobile tactics evolving in South East Asia.

Few will forget the sound. A low rhythmic thump that grew second by second until the machine had passed, leaving behind only the mechanical hum of a turbine. This was the real soundtrack to the rock-and-roll war, for the Bell Huey and its distinctive rotor chop were heard the length and breadth of South Vietnam from 1962 until 1975.

Far from ending its career with its massive airlift effort during the final 'Frequent Wind' evacuation from Saigon, the Huey has gone on to equip the helicopter squadrons of air arms around the world, and is still the most numerous helicopter in the US Army, with an amazing 3,500 in service.

Bell had been a major influence in early helicopter design, and their Model 47/H-13 Sioux range had become the standard utility/training helicopter for the West. During the mid-1950s the adaptation of the

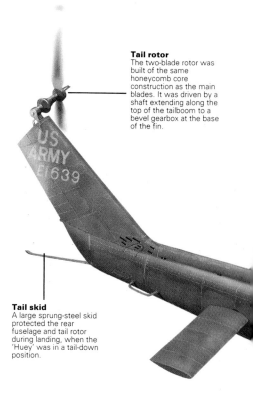

Tail rotor
The two-blade rotor was built of the same honeycomb core construction as the main blades. It was driven by a shaft extending along the top of the tailboom to a bevel gearbox at the base of the fin.

Tail skid
A large sprung-steel skid protected the rear fuselage and tail rotor during landing, when the 'Huey' was in a tail-down position.

Supported by an AH-1 Cobra, a flight of Hueys approaches Bu Dop Special Forces camp after a patrol along the Cambodian border. Note the pintle-mounted 7.62-mm machine-guns in the cabin doors.

turboshaft engine to helicopter propulsion offered great promise to designers, the new units offering unrivalled power at low weights. One of the best powerplants was the Lycoming T-53, which was adopted by Bell for a new assault ship for the Army.

Winning design

The Model 204 was a classic, incorporating the latest in helicopter design. It was easily the winner of a 1955 design competition. After a very rapid design and construction phase, the first aircraft flew on 22 October 1956, with the Army designation XH-40. Production of the HU-1A followed, the first deliveries being made in June 1959. Despite its official name Iroquois, it was universally dubbed the 'Huey' because of its designation.

In 1962 the designations were reshuffled and the helicopter became the UH-1A, coincident with its first deployment to South East Asia. The first use was in the escort role, with aircraft hastily adapted to carry forward-firing 7.62-mm machine-guns and rocket pods. The more powerful UH-1B introduced shortly afterwards offered greater armament capabilities, adding the familiar door-mounted guns as well as greater forward-firing power.

Crewed throughout its career by two pilots, the 'Huey' in its UH-1B form could initially take seven troops, and it was quickly pressed into service as an assault transport, being powerful enough and manoeuvrable enough to enter landing zones (LZs), deposit its load, and exit at great speed and at low level. So the Hueys split into two roles that would involve huge numbers of aircraft throughout the Vietnam involvement.

From early in its career the UH-1 has been used for casualty evacuation, and this role was especially important in Vietnam. It is still undertaken today, as practised here by this UH-1H in Germany.

Inside the 'Huey'

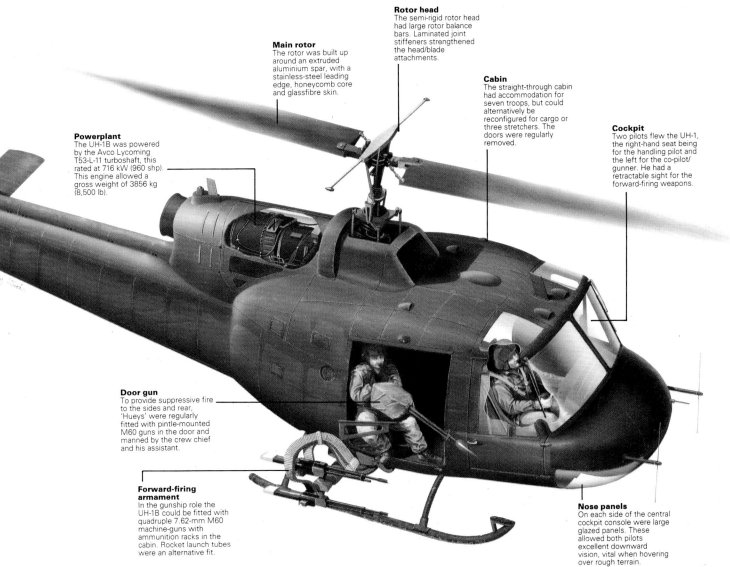

Rotor head
The semi-rigid rotor head had large rotor balance bars. Laminated joint stiffeners strengthened the head/blade attachments.

Main rotor
The rotor was built up around an extruded aluminium spar, with a stainless-steel leading edge, honeycomb core and glassfibre skin.

Cabin
The straight-through cabin had accommodation for seven troops, but could alternatively be reconfigured for cargo or three stretchers. The doors were regularly removed.

Cockpit
Two pilots flew the UH-1, the right-hand seat being for the handling pilot and the left for the co-pilot/gunner. He had a retractable sight for the forward-firing weapons.

Powerplant
The UH-1B was powered by the Avco Lycoming T53-L-11 turboshaft, this rated at 716 kW (960 shp). This engine allowed a gross weight of 3856 kg (8,500 lb).

Door gun
To provide suppressive fire to the sides and rear, 'Hueys' were regularly fitted with pintle-mounted M60 guns in the door and manned by the crew chief and his assistant.

Forward-firing armament
In the gunship role the UH-1B could be fitted with quadruple 7.62-mm M60 machine-guns with ammunition racks in the cabin. Rocket launch tubes were an alternative fit.

Nose panels
On each side of the central cockpit console were large glazed panels. These allowed both pilots excellent downward vision, vital when hovering over rough terrain.

Assault transports

Firstly there were the 'slicks'. These were the assault transports, carrying troops into the thick of battle and extracting them when battle was done. Large-scale setpiece attacks involved large numbers of Hueys, who flew low and in train to their LZ, landing in lines and departing almost in unison. In such a way, a sizeable ground force could be landed or extracted in seconds. Other roles such as resupply and cargo transport were also the domain of these aircraft.

On the other hand there were the 'hogs' – the gunships. Heavily armed, they rode 'shotgun' for the 'slicks', protecting the main assault force and suppressing fire during operations around the LZ. Bearing guns and rockets (and even TOW missiles on a

handful of machines), the 'hogs' played a huge part in airmobile operations, well after the dedicated AH-1 Cobra reached Asia.

Huey development continued with the UH-1C dedicated gunship, and the Model 205 UH-1D which introduced a larger cabin that could accommodate 12 troops or six stretchers. The similar UH-1H had an uprated engine and became the major production model, and the one still in widespread service today. One other Army variant was the UH-1M, which was a UH-1C fitted with night attack equipment.

Throughout the war the Huey accompanied the Army everywhere, and the UH-1 became as familiar a sight in-country as the M16. Virtually everything that was moved went by Huey, and that meant mainly people.

Troops rode to battle by Huey, commanders looking on from command ships. Key personnel moved from headquarters to operational areas by Huey. 'Dustoff' Hueys flew into battles to retrieve the wounded and move them on their way to hospital. 'Bullshit bombers' dropped leaflets while 'bugships' sprayed pesticide around villages – no job was too big or too small for the UH-1, and it answered uncomplainingly.

The sheer numbers meant that VC gunners got a lot of practice shooting at it, and despite the attentions of the 'hogs' and door gunners, huge numbers fell. At the final reckoning the US Army lost one to a MiG, one to a SAM, 1,095 to AAA, 114 to air base attacks and 1,380 to operational losses, making a grand total of 2,591.

The US Army was supported in Vietnam by South Vietnamese and Australian forces, the latter bringing their own Hueys with them. This heavily-armed 'hog' takes a break in the jungle while a 'slick' lands behind.

Some were armed with a six-barrel 7.62-mm Minigun for fire suppression. Later 20 UH-1Fs were converted to UH-1P standard, which were equipped for psychological warfare duties. Today a handful of UH-1N and HH-1N twin-engined Hueys fly on in support and rescue roles.

While the United States accounts for the majority of the Hueys built, many other nations (63 at the last count!) have adopted various members of the Huey family for their assault transport forces. Several have seen action, including those of Argentina, Burma, El Salvador, Honduras, Iran, Israel, Laos, Thailand and South Vietnam.

Marine gunships

Of course the US Army was not the only user of this classic helicopter. US Marine Corps units were issued with the UH-1E gunship for Vietnam duty, while later the UH-1N twin-engined development has been procured for service from assault carriers. The US Navy also uses this model, in addition to various single-engined versions, some of which were used for light attack during riverine patrols in the Mekong Delta.

US Air Force Hueys were originally procured to support strategic missile sites, but many of these General Electric T58-powered UH-1Fs ended up in South East Asia, flying clandestine support missions with Special Forces.

In difficult terrain troopers had to jump the last few feet to the ground. Here a UH-1H 'slick' deposits its cargo on a Vietnamese hilltop.

The UH-1 will have a large part to play in US Army operations until at least the end of the century. Army National Guard units are now the main operators, front-line units having adopted the UH-60A Black Hawk.

Mass licence production

With such a successful design, it is not unnatural that mass licence production has taken place. Indonesia, Japan, South Korea, Thailand and West Germany have all built Hueys, but the major source overseas is Italy, where Agusta continues to be a major producer of the Huey family. Indeed Agusta has developed its own versions, notably the AB 212ASW specialist anti-submarine version.

Despite being replaced in front-line US Army units by the Sikorsky UH-60 Black Hawk, the Huey shows no signs of ageing. More and more aircraft are swelling the Army National Guard units, and the US Army aims to keep 2,700 in service into the next century. Only a handful of other nations can afford to replace their aircraft, so the Huey will be a feature for many years to come.

THE US CAVALRY

One of the abiding images of the Vietnam War was of soldiers leaping into battle from UH-1 'Huey' helicopters. The Cavalry were the first and best exponents of such air assault tactics.

The history of the US Cavalry is almost as old as that of the United States. A number of the heroes of the War of Independence were cavalrymen. They included 'Light Horse' Harry Lee, who fought as a British light cavalryman during the Seven Years War, and who late in life was to father Robert E. Lee, one of America's greatest soldiers and the commander of the Confederate forces during the Civil War.

In the early days, American cavalry followed the European pattern, designed to act as reconnaissance units and as shock troops in battle, but gradually the reconnaissance role became more important.

During the American Civil War, their principal task was to scout out enemy positions and formations, and to act as a screen behind which infantry and artillery units could prepare their battle lines. The primary use of the horse was to provide mobility, and in combat cavalrymen often dismounted to skirmish on foot.

The essence of cavalry tactics lay in combining helicopters, armour and foot soldiers into a cohesive whole, able to operate in any terrain.

Cavalrymen like Jeb Stuart, Wade Hampton and Nathan Bedford Forrest seemed to be the epitome of the Southern cavalier style of warfare, whereas Northern cavalrymen were perhaps less dashing, with some exceptions like George Armstrong Custer. By the end of the war, however, the efficient Northern cavalry under the leadership of General Sheridan had become dominant.

In the Indian Wars, the cavalry

After Vietnam, the cavalry changed dramatically. In Germany, cavalry units became heavy armoured formations with tanks and infantry fighting vehicles, like the M1 Abrams and M2 Bradley.

change yet again. With the prospect of conflict breaking out almost anywhere in the world, cavalry units will have to become even more mobile. Indeed, the most recent use of cavalry was in this type of out-of-area role. Cavalry units were heavily involved in the 1991 Gulf War. The US VII and XVIII Corps included the 1st Cavalry Division, the 2nd Cavalry Regiment and the 3rd Cavalry Regiment. The 82nd Airborne and 101st Air Assault Divisions both played key roles, being used in the air assault role pioneered by the air cavalry in Vietnam.

Below: The cavalry saw a considerable amount of combat in the Gulf War. Some units acted in the classic cavalry fashion, seeking out enemy positions by ranging far ahead of the main armoured force.

Below: The new cavalry units are far more powerful than they were in previous conflicts. In the Gulf they formed part of the powerful coalition armoured force, which used the latest M1A1 Main Battle Tanks to smash through Iraq's Republican Guard.

came into its own, since the only way to fix an elusive, highly-mobile enemy over the vast distances of the American West was to be just as mobile. Sometimes the cavalry was successful, but on other occasions, most notably when Custer's Seventh Cavalry took on the entire Sioux nation on the banks of the Little Bighorn River, the result was disaster.

During World War II the horse was replaced by light mechanised vehicles, but the cavalry functions of reconnaissance and screening remained essentially unchanged. In Vietnam, some cavalry units carried out traditional roles, but others had become heavy armoured units, operating with M48 Main Battle Tanks.

It was during the Vietnam War that an entirely new cavalry concept arose. The rapid development of the helicopter in the 1950s led the US Army to produce an entirely new kind of formation to make use of the aircraft's unique abilities. Using large numbers of helicopters, a division could make an airborne assault and seize control of large areas of territory in a very short space of time.

1st Cavalry Division

The 11th Air Assault Division (Test) proved the concept at Fort Benning, in Georgia. It was considered ideal for the kind of war which was emerging in Vietnam, and the 11th, renamed the 1st Cavalry Division (Airmobile), was sent to South East Asia in 1965. The division was assembled and rushed to the combat theatre in record time; the normal bureaucratic stumbling blocks being swept aside. Although untried in combat, the air cavalry proved highly successful. From fierce combat in the Ia Drang Valley in 1965, through

the relief of Khe Sanh in 1968, to the massive incursion into Cambodia in 1970, the 'Cav' set the pace for the rest of the US troops in Vietnam.

Changing role

After the war, the cavalry changed its role once again. The 1st Armored Cavalry Division, based at Fort Hood in Texas, is a heavy tank formation, designed to be used at the spearhead of a major conflict. Independent cavalry regiments are powerful brigade-sized units that perform some of the old cavalry tasks, but in vastly greater strength than previously. For instance, the 11th Armored Cavalry Regiment, the 'Black Horse' regiment, was forward deployed in Germany's Fulda Gap. Equipped with M1 Abrams tanks and M2 Bradley fighting vehicles, as well as with an air cavalry component, the 11th's task was to cover the mobilisation of the US Army's VII Corps in the face of a Soviet advance in Central Europe.

With the end of the Cold War, it is likely that the cavalry's role will

JOINT OPERATIONS

Attack helicopters, although strong individual weapons, don't operate alone and unsupported. There are times when you can make good use of ground-based combat support, especially air defence artillery, and ground-to-ground fire support such as artillery, mortars and even naval gunfire. On top of that you work closely with the second-echelon support services such as intelligence and engineering units.

Combat support is provided by the ground forces for whom you're working at the time, and it's controlled by the ground force commander. He has the responsibility and the command, and he will co-ordinate the support available, switching from one sector to another depending on need and the resources available.

Combat support can be direct – applying artillery fire on a precise map reference to take out a particular enemy position; general – providing suppressive fire over a wider area; or attached – moving and working

In the Cold War scenario which dominated NATO thinking for 40 years, it was not envisaged that the helicopters would take on Soviet tanks alone. Attack helicopters will co-operate with NATO close air support (CAS) aircraft like this US Air Force A-10, seen here firing a Maverick missile.

The helicopter attack must be co-ordinated with friendly artillery. As the AH-64 engages enemy armour with its Hellfire anti-tank missiles, US artillery fires shells fitted with VT fuses which burst in the air above the tanks. This forces the tanks to close down, sharply reducing their visibility and preventing most tanks from firing their anti-aircraft machine-gun.

ARTILLERY AID FOR ATTACK HELICOPTERS

1. **Directed by scout helicopters, artillery can force the tanks to close down before the attack, making it very difficult for them to locate the attack helicopters.**
2. **By keeping enemy armoured vehicles closed down their rate of advance is also slowed, and it is harder for them to co-ordinate their defence.**
3. **The radar system of the dreaded ZSU-23-4 anti-aircraft gun is vulnerable to shell splinters and can be knocked out by an artillery barrage.**
4. **Units adjacent to the ones being attacked by the helicopters can be suppressed by artillery to stop them interfering with the helicopter attack.**

SEQUENTIAL ATTACKS

When a target area is small or the avenues of approach are limited, attack helicopters and A-10 aircraft attack in turns. While the jets are making their attack, the helicopters can manoeuvre to new firing positions so that the enemy vehicles are hit from a different direction after each pass from the aircraft.

An A-10 fires a Maverick missile at an enemy tank, then pulls out to let the helicopters make their attack

The A-10 flies out of the way while the helicopters make their attack in turn

directly with the attack helicopter unit. Engineering and intelligence support fall into this category.

An attack helicopter may seem, to enemy ground forces, to be moving so fast that it doesn't provide a possible target. But to enemy aircraft, with their much wider field of vision and superior speed and weapons systems, they're very vulnerable.

Cover and concealment are your best defence, but there's also general support from Air Defence Artillery (ADA). This support is provided on an area basis, not dedicated to individual aircraft. Most ADA is computer-controlled, picking up and tracking any aircraft that comes into its sector, so it's vital that all friendly aircraft can identify themselves to the gunnery control system automatically – there won't be time to respond manually!

COMBINED ATTACK

This demands split-second timing. The aircraft and the helicopters do not attack at exactly the same moment; instead, the helicopters begin their attack as the jets approach the target. As the A-10s pull up to launch their missiles, the helicopters pop back into cover and attack again as the aircraft complete their escape manoeuvre and leave the target area.

Helicopters fire just before and just after the A-10s attack

A-10s pull up to fire their missiles then escape under covering fire from the helicopters.

This system is known as IFF (Identification Friend or Foe), and is in the form of a radio beacon that transmits a coded message. Check that it's working – regularly – and make very sure that you know all the appropriate code settings. There are three stages of 'alert status' for ADA systems:

1 Weapons Hold: fire only in self-defence

2 Weapons Tight: fire only at aircraft positively identified as hostile

3 Weapons Free: fire on any aircraft not positively identified as friendly.

Enemy armour

One of the most effective uses of direct fire support is to take out enemy ADA to allow you to get on with your main task – destroying enemy armour. The support can be distant: from field artillery units or, if you're within contact range, from a naval task force lying off the coast. Or it can be local, coming from the attacking infantry company's own mortars.

Mortars can also be used against dismounted infantry whose man-portable anti-tank/anti-aircraft systems are proving troublesome, and also to provide illumination. Because of their high trajectory, mortar rounds are particularly effective against units located in dead ground such as the far side of a ridge, where you can't get at them without coming into range of their ADA fire yourself.

Where possible, a member of the artillery unit will fly with the attack helicopters, probably as observer in one of the scouts. He's specially trained to call down supporting fire with the least possible delay. This may not always be possible, however, so you must be able to do the job yourself should it be necessary. The artillery arm provides training officers for attack helicopter units for this purpose.

Suppression

If the target proves particularly difficult, and can't be suppressed even by a combined attack helicopter/artillery support operation, then the next step is to call in the air force.

A close air support mission (CAS) is run by the air force alone; the only thing you might be asked to do is to provide transportation for the forward air controller (FAC).

But that's not to say that you'll be loitering in the rear somewhere! The CAS, if properly controlled and co-ordinated, will leave the enemy in a state of chaos – but not for long, if you're facing well-led, battle-hardened troops. You'll have only a few moments in which to exploit the advantage the CAS gives you. Using cover and concealment techniques, you wait in the holding area, taking your attack timing from the forward air controller.

Joint air attack

The most difficult support operation to mount, control and co-ordinate is the joint air attack team (JAAT) operation. In any operation that involves ground forces, supporting artillery, attack helicopters and close air support, all working together, there is bound to be some confusion.

Briefing a JAAT

Because of the difficulties and complexities in controlling an operation where four different types of offensive troops are deployed, the longer the period involved between thinking up the operation and it taking place, the better – so long as your security is tight – to allow really comprehensive briefing and planning.

Each member of the JAAT task force must supply a minimum of information – the close air support team, for instance, will supply details of the types of weapons they have available and how long they can loiter (stay over the engagement area looking for other targets to hit).

All this 'asset information' is co-ordinated and a plan of attack put

SECTOR ATTACK

Sector attacks are the easiest to manage and they reduce the risk of friendly aircraft endangering each other during the attack. The aircraft attack one part of the target while the helicopters deal with another. Both units attack independently and do not have to co-ordinate their firing.

Helicopters engage targets in their designated sector

The road marks the dividing line between the sectors

A-10s attack targets in their designated sector

together that makes the best use of what's available.

The CAS aircraft – probably A-10s – are built to take anti-aircraft fire. They go in first, flying nap-of-the-earth from the holding area, transmitting intelligence back to the battle commander so that he keeps an up-to-date picture of

the situation. The strike aircraft are followed closely by the attack helicopters flying at even lower level.

When the CAS team is over the target, the level of air defence artillery fire will increase as the enemy opens up with everything he's got; that's just what the attack helicopters are wait-

An A-10 opens fire with its 30-mm GAU-8 cannon, which have a core of depleted uranium to bore through enemy tank armour. For this reason the latest Soviet tanks are being fitted with extra armour on the turret.

Its armoured skin pierced by a hail of 30-mm shells, a tank disintegrates as its fuel and ammunition explodes. NATO ground forces rely heavily on the ability of tactical aircraft and helicopters to destroy enemy armour.

The Bell AH-1 Cobra was the first of the specialist gunship helicopters. Modern anti-armour tactics use the helicopter as a kind of flying artillery, using rockets, guns and missiles.

When the target warrants it, the two airborne arms can work even more closely together, in combined attack. Both engaging the targets at the same time, they can be fairly certain that whatever countermeasures the enemy takes, he won't be able to acquire enough of the targets to prevent his destruction.

Below: The McDonnell AH-64 Apache was deployed to the Gulf in the fight against Saddam Hussein. Most of the time it operated so far ahead of allied troops that it was impossible to set up joint attack teams.

ing for. With every target identified and acquired by the scout helicopters in their stand-off positions, the enemy ADA can now be taken out by air-to-ground missiles operating from outside the anti-aircraft guns' effective range.

Close air support

With effective training you will be very much more comfortable with JAAT missions. Experience shows that a bare minimum of information – target location, description and attack time – are all that's needed to set up an effective helicopter/CAS operation.

When these two very different types of aircraft operate together in ground strike operations, there are three basic strategies available:

1 Sector attack
2 Sequential attack
3 Combined attack

Sector attack is the most straightforward. The two parts of the assault force are each assigned to a sector of the engagement area, and operate separately while still supporting each other.

If the engagement area is small, or the avenues of attack narrow and limited, it may be necessary to mount a sequential attack – helicopters and strike aircraft attacking one after the other to vary the characteristics of the attack and the types of weapons used, to make life more difficult for the defenders on the ground.

In practice, this becomes a sort of three-dimensional fire-and-movement exercise. The CAS aircraft engage the target while the helicopters are taking up their positions. As the A-10s break off, the helicopters unmask, acquire their targets, and fire their weapons. During the time the enemy is occupied with the helicopters' ATGMs, the A-10s have taken a new avenue of attack and resume the engagement with their Avenger cannon and rockets.

Below: The anti-armour missile has given attack helicopters like the Cobra the power to strike at enemy tanks from well beyond the range of short-range anti-air weapons, and by operating at low level such helicopters can keep clear of the threat envelope of longer-ranged systems.

POUNCE
WITH THE PUMA

A Puma of the Aviation Legère de l'Armée de Terre operating in the assault role delivers a squad of French infantrymen into combat. The Puma can carry 16 fully-equipped troops into battle.

You're waiting in the trees. Your stomach is knotted up into a tight ball of tension and fear. You can hear the rising throb of approaching helicopters, and you strain to catch sight of them. The briefing was straightforward enough: a large force of troops is moving east by road to counter a massive enemy armoured and airborne thrust, and they're inserting a recce patrol by air at the intended destination to make sure it's clear of enemy troops. It's Day One of the war, and you're part of the patrol.

You don't see the Pumas until the last moment, when they lift out of a shallow valley that you wouldn't have believed was deep enough to hide them. Those pilots must really know their stuff. The first Puma comes to a low hover, its rotors kicking up swir-

ling clouds of dust and sand which burn your eyes and throat. The huge aircraft settles on its wheels and the helmeted figure in the open door

raises his thumb. You're clear to emplane. You run to the aircraft in a low crouch, aware of the spinning rotors close above your head.

You scramble into the Puma and slide back along the cabin into one of the sideways-facing canvas seats, fingers fumbling with the simple lap strap. The noise is incredible, and

The SADF uses the Puma as its standard assault and transport helicopter, employing it during the bush war on the Angolan border and in Namibia.

Inside the Puma

This Aérospatiale Puma carries the markings of No. 33 Squadron, a UK-based support helicopter unit which operates in support of regular and territorial army units. During the Cold War, the squadron would have deployed in support of NATO's AMF, perhaps to Norway or perhaps somewhere along the central front.

'Hockeystick'
This projecting skid prevents the tail rotor from contacting the ground during tail-down manoeuvres close to the ground.

Tail rotor
The tail rotor sideways thrust to counteract the torque effect of the main rotor, preventing the helicopter from spinning around under the rotor.

VHF radio aerial

Cabin
The Puma's long and spacious cabin can accommodate freight or up to 16 troops on outward-facing canvas seats.

Nitesun
The Nitesun searchlight is electrically driven and remotely controlled, sending out a focusable beam of light sufficient to turn 'night into day' on the ground.

Crewman
The crewman, usually a senior NCO, is responsible for the helicopters load, whether it is underslung or carried inside the cabin. He also assists the pilot with navigation and keeping a lookout for enemy aircraft.

Underslung load hook
The belly hook can lift loads of up to 2,500 kg, allowing a wide variety of loads to be carried, including the 105-mm Light Gun.

when everyone is strapped in it rises to a crescendo and the helicopter rises into the air. The nose seems to dip and the helicopter accelerates. You're facing outwards, and there's a small square window in front of you. The ground whips past at enormous speed and it seems very close, but looking forward through the narrow entrance into the cockpit you can see that the pilot in the right-hand seat looks un-

You approach a helicopter from the front, when the pilot signals that you are clear to emplane. This allows the crew to keep you in sight and ensures that you won't run into the tail rotor.

concerned as he guides the helicopter under the high-tension cables.

There are a couple of times when you think you've arrived. The aircraft lands briefly, but the crewman doesn't signal you to deplane. If there are any enemy troops around they won't know where you've actually been dropped, giving you a huge tactical advantage. Arriving at the drop-off point, the crewman pulls the doors open. You can't hear anything over the noise of the engines, but he seems to be talking the pilot down, as if he were reversing into a tight parking space.

There's a GPMG (general purpose machine-gun) mounted in the door-way, but it wouldn't be much use against enemy aircraft, and they're dropping you well behind the front line. It's not like those Vietnam War films you've seen where you go into a 'Hot' LZ (landing zone) with all guns blazing. In Western Europe you seem

*Heavily armed groundcrew in **NBC** kit are dug in around the landing field. A nucleus of **RAF Regiment** personnel train the squadron groundcrew in site defence in peacetime, and supervise site defence on exercise or in war.*

Main rotor
The composite four-bladed main rotor is extremely damage-resistant and can be quickly folded for ease of storage.

Engine
The Puma is powered by a pair of powerful Turboméca Turmo III C4 turboshaft engines, mounted side-by-side above the cabin on a titanium structure.

Pilot
The pilot sits in the right-hand seat. During peacetime the left-hand seat is usually left empty.

Radar warning receiver
Nose- and tail-mounted RWRs warn the pilot when the aircraft is being illuminated by hostile radars, giving details of the nature and bearing of the threat.

Machine-gun
A 7.62-mm GPMG can be mounted in the Puma's doorway. Opposed assaults against defended landing zones are a thing of the past, so the Puma's gun is primarily a morale-booster.

Undercarriage
The Puma is fitted with a hydraulically semi-retractable tricycle undercarriage. When retracted it generates appreciably less drag.

A landing Puma generates a huge downwash, kicking up dust and small stones over a wide area. The aircraft are fitted with polyvalent air intakes which filter the air before it goes through the engines.

to try to keep out of sight of the enemy, keeping your vulnerable helicopters well away from enemy groundfire, SAMs or fighters.

You leap out of the helicopter as soon as it lands and form a defensive circle around it. Have they seen you arrive? They certainly couldn't avoid hearing you. The engines bellow and the helicopter lifts off, accelerating away before plunging down and vanishing into another valley.

The Westland Aérospatiale Puma is an Anglo-French design, and more than 1,000 have been sold to several countries since it first flew in 1965. The users include South Africa, who have designed a dedicated gunship version of the aircraft and who have used the basic support helicopter version in action during raids into Angola and other neighbouring countries. French army Pumas have been used in combat in Chad.

Support Helicopter Force

The Puma forms the backbone of the RAF's Support Helicopter Force, with two front-line squadrons, one based in Britain and one in Germany. The British-based squadron operates in support of UKLF (UK Land Forces), UKMF (UK Mobile Forces) and NATO's AMF (Allied Commander Europe Mobile Forces), and can be found operating beside the British Army all over Europe, from Norway to Turkey and anywhere in between. The German-based squadron operates in support of the British Army of the Rhine.

A detachment of four Pumas is permanently based in Belize, operating in support of the British garrison there, resupplying remote OPs on the Guatemalan border and inserting, resupplying and recovering patrols in the dense jungle. Closer to home a single Puma is deployed in Northern Ire-

A 'desert pink' Royal Air Force Puma 'spools up' before setting off on a mission during the Gulf War. A composite squadron of Pumas drawn from RAF Odiham and RAF Gütersloh supported British troops in Saudi Arabia and Kuwait.

land, operating in the night reconnaissance and Special Forces support roles. The Puma can easily be transported inside a C-130 Hercules, and this makes overseas deployments even easier.

High-speed transport

The Puma's main role is to transport men and equipment at high speed to where it is most needed. A helicopter can cross any terrain, and does not require roads, bridges, or even airfields. This makes it extremely versatile, and very useful. Unfortunately there is a great shortage of support helicopters, so it isn't usually possible to transport large troop formations by air. Instead, the Puma force can be used to drop off reconnaissance teams, and a small body of troops who can hold a position until the bulk of the force arrives by road.

The Puma has a long and spacious cabin, and this can quickly be fitted with up to 16 canvas seats or six standard NATO stretchers, or it can be left empty so that large pieces of equipment can be carried internally. A winch can be fitted above the starboard door, allowing troops to be extracted from clearings too small to land in. To get into such clearings, it's usually quicker to abseil, although they can also be winched down.

The RAF's Pumas are fitted with a belly-mounted cargo hook, and this allows heavy, bulky or awkward loads to be carried underslung, beneath the helicopter, instead of in the cabin. This makes loading and unloading much quicker, and loads can be jettisoned if enemy fighters try to intervene. There are disadvantages, of course. The pilot has to fly higher, to

give the load clearance above the ground, increasing the danger of being seen or appearing on enemy radar screens, and increasing his vulnerability to hostile ground fire.

The Puma is powered by a pair of powerful Rolls Royce Turboméca Turmo IIIC4 turboshafts, giving the aircraft an excellent performance with high cruising speed and excellent manoeuvrability compared with the Wessex which it replaced. The newer Super Puma has an advanced technology main rotor, new engines and uprated transmission, and a larger cabin accommodating up to 25 troops compared with the 16 carried by the standard Puma.

Below: France has developed an improved version called the Super Puma or the Cougar. This Exocet-armed example is used for anti-ship missions.

A flight of Pumas approaches a landing zone. Five such helicopters can deliver nearly 100 troops into action, with a speed and precision unmatched by any other means of military transport.

BUSH HELICOPTER TACTICS

The cabin of a troop-carrying helicopter going into battle is a confusing place. The noise is truly ear-shattering, and every available space is cluttered with essential equipment and a jostling crowd of excited men keyed up to fever pitch. Time after time heliborne operations ('heliops') have proved their worth in anti-terrorist and counter-insurgency campaigns. This is the first section on Bush Warfare, and shows how the South African Defence Force uses helicopters as combat and support craft in anti-terrorist operations.

The helicopter's main strength in combat is its ability to get troops into areas that they could otherwise reach only on foot, perhaps after days of cross-country marching. It gets them there so quickly that a successful operation can be mounted before the enemy has any idea that they're aware of his presence.

Because airborne operations take place at such high speed, it's extra-important that each member of the aircrew and the airborne troop knows exactly what he has to do at all times. Helicopters are expensive to operate –

every hour of flight costs many hundreds of pounds – and have only a short radius of action.

Know your job

Helicopter drill has two purposes: to cut down time wasted through mistakes; and to make sure that both aircraft and personnel stay as safe as

possible. There are no short cuts. Everyone concerned has to do things

Fire Force in action: South African soldiers fly into action aboard an Aérospatiale Puma helicopter. They are kept on standby to launch instant attacks on terrorist gangs the moment they are discovered by patrols, hidden observers or aerial reconnaissance.

STICK LEADER'S PRE-FLIGHT DUTIES

As the leader of the stick, you must make a series of checks before the helicopter is airborne. Once in the air you use the spare headset to communicate with the pilots and keep an eye on the ground over which you will be operating.

1. Brief the men on the signals that will be used during emplaning and deplaning.
2. Ensure that everyone has taken off their caps or jungle hats.
3. Check that no-one is loosely carrying equipment such as water bottles, machetes, ammunition pouches etc.
4. Make sure that all straps on packs and equipment are tucked away.
5. Remove the aerials from the radios and stow them away.
6. Check that weapon slings are tight, carrying handles folded down and that bayonets are not fixed.
7. Check that all weapons safety precautions have been observed.

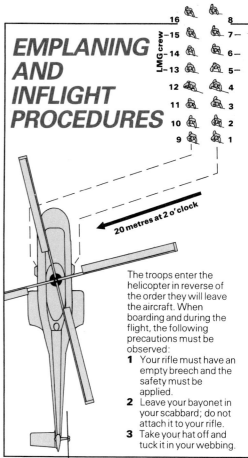

EMPLANING AND INFLIGHT PROCEDURES

20 metres at 2 o'clock

The troops enter the helicopter in reverse of the order they will leave the aircraft. When boarding and during the flight, the following precautions must be observed:

1 Your rifle must have an empty breech and the safety must be applied.
2 Leave your bayonet in your scabbard; do not attach it to your rifle.
3 Take your hat off and tuck it in your webbing.

---

exactly by the book. When the order comes to start a heliborne operation, the stick leader must make sure that each member of the team knows his place and what to do immediately after leaving the aircraft. He should form his squad up in reverse of the order they will leave the aircraft. Then he waits for the pilot's signal to emplane – a clear nod of the head and a thumbs-up sign, for example. When in the helicopter it is vital that no infantryman interferes with the crew, and that no-one touches any of the controls.

Overwhelming noise

The noise in a helicopter is quite deafening. The stick leader should always put on the spare headset so that he can communicate with the pilot and any other crew members.

Weapons safety, at all times, is vitally important. A round fired off by accident could hit a vital piece of machinery and cost the life of everyone aboard. For this reason weapons must be carried with the breech cleared. On those rare occasions when the stick has to come out of the aircraft fighting, then the weapon can be charged and cocked, but the safety must be on, to make it impossible to loose off a round by accident. Because of the cramped conditions, bayonets should never in any circumstances be fixed on board.

The man in charge

The pilot is in command of the aircraft at all times. He is responsible for it, and for every person on board. His commands must be obeyed immediately. He alone decides how many men can be carried, and when and how they will enter and leave the aircraft. For operational reasons, he transmits his orders through the stick commander.

The stick commander also has his

Troops relax en route to the landing zone in the operational area up-country in southern Africa. The mood will soon change once they've landed in a hostile area.

own responsibilities. These are mainly to do with the safety of his men and how they behave in the aircraft, but he must also pay attention to the ground they are above, looking for possible future landing sites, useful terrain features such as sources of fresh water and potential defensive positions, and, of course, signs of the enemy.

Contact!

The real strength of heliborne counter-insurgency operations is the speed with which they can be mounted. Experience of actual operations has

shown SADF that concealed static observation posts are much more effective in gathering intelligence about enemy movements than mobile patrols. A patrol moving cross-country gives itself away very easily, especially by being seen and reported to guerrillas by civilian sympathisers. These static OPs must be in constant

LANDING ZONE PROCEDURES

Just as counter-insurgency troops rely on the helicopter crew to get them safely in and out of the battle, the pilot and crew depend on the men on the ground to carry out certain tasks.

Clearing and marking the LZ is the most important job. A heavily-laden helicopter can't land or take off straight up and down. When it's full of cargo or passengers, it behaves more like

an ordinary aircraft, and must land and take off at a shallow angle. A track must be cleared so that the pilot can bring the aircraft safely into and out of the LZ.

Another advantage the helicopter does have over fixed-wing aircraft, however, is that it is much less influenced by the wind direction when landing and at take-off. Instead of having to head into the wind at take-off, the

helicopter pilot has a wider choice: he only has to pay attention to wind direction when it's really strong. This in turn makes the ground crew's job a lot easier – the same LZ can be used in all sorts of conditions.

At night the LZ must be marked with lights. Five is the best number, arranged in the shape of a T, with the top bar into the wind if this is important. Otherwise the bar will be opposite the shallowest possible approach path.

Battery torches are a good source of light. They should be placed 10 metres apart, with the beams shining up at an angle of

Puma landing zone

To land safely, a Puma helicopter needs a landing zone at least 50 metres in diameter, with a central area 35 metres in diameter cleared to ground level. At the centre of the LZ there must be a hard surface 15 metres in diameter.

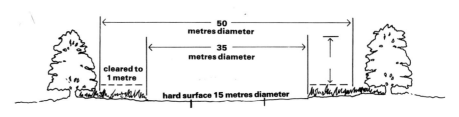

50 metres diameter

35 metres diameter

cleared to 1 metre

hard surface 15 metres diameter

HAND SIGNALS

The noise inside a helicopter makes voice communications practically impossible so hand signals are used:

Emplaning signal (day): Pilot or crew member gives the thumbs up or vigorously nods his head. It is now safe to approach the helicopter (in a stooped attitude, to avoid the rotors).

Emplaning signal (night): Intermittent flashing of the helicopter navigation lights.

Do not emplane yet: Pilot or crew member raises open right hand with the palm outwards.

Some members of the stick to emplane: Pilot or crew member extends a number of fingers indicating how many men are to board the helicopter.

Prepare to deplane: Pilot or crew member motions with his left hand.

Target direction: This is indicated by the pilot or crew member pointing.

Deplane: Pilot or crew member nods his head vigorously. You must now exit the plane in the pre-arranged order as fast as you can.

SEATING PLAN

1 The stick leader is last into and first out of the helicopter.

2 The LMG crews sit nearest the doors and operate the machine-guns as protection.

3 In a crisis, 24 men may be loaded, at sea level only.

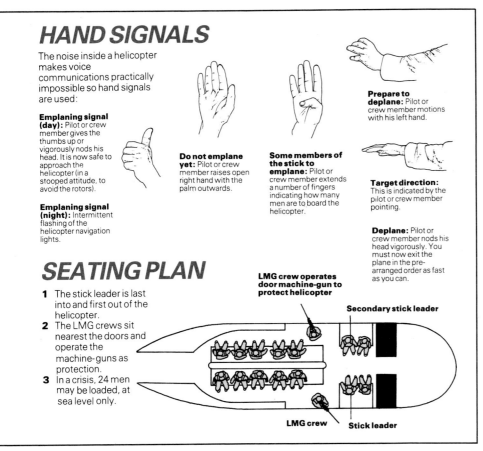

LMG crew operates door machine-gun to protect helicopter

Secondary stick leader

LMG crew **Stick leader**

radio contact with the operational base.

When a report of terrorist activity comes in, it should be only a matter of moments before assault troops are called together for a briefing. This will include all the essential information about the contact: map reference, a short report of the circumstances, the number of assault troops required, whether they are to be supported by helicopter gunships or other air strikes, how they are to approach the target, rendezvous (RV) position with troops already on the ground, and the radio frequencies, call signs and passwords that are to be used for the operation.

All this can be accomplished in the time it takes the aircrews to warm up the helicopters and carry out their pre-launch checks. Within minutes, the assault sticks can be out on the dispersal point, waiting for the signal to emplane.

Troop commander

The troop commander always travels in the helicopter gunship. If there is no gunship support, he has to travel in the lead troop carrier. Where a gunship is involved in the operation, it must be possible for friendly ground forces to identify it easily. The best way to achieve this is by means of a series of smoke grenades, tied to the step or undercarriage of the gunship, and triggered by the troop commander.

Going in to land

When the assault force arrives at the RV, contact with the forces who have spotted the enemy will make sure that the commander has up-to-date information about the guerrillas' behaviour. While the troop carriers orbit the RV on a high and wide course, the ship carrying the troop commander goes in low, so that he can see the enemy disposition for himself. The observers in the static OP should have reported the presence of any anti-aircraft weaponry with the guerrilla band, and the troop commander must bear this in mind when deciding how close to the enemy he can get. Where

between 30 and 40 degrees. Because the helicopter's main rotor generates a very powerful down-draught, the torches must be partly buried in the ground, to prevent them being blown over.

If there are more than five torches to hand, the number of individual lights is not increased. Instead, two torches are used at each location, one angled as before, the other pointing straight up into the sky.

Other light sources can be used instead of torches. Hurricane lamps or pressure lamps are both good enough and, as a last resort, sand in an open-ended tin can be soaked with a gallon of petrol and set alight. The helicopter pilot will bring his craft to land slightly to the left of the three lights that form the vertical line of the T, so the lights are best placed slightly to the right of centre of the LZ.

In an emergency, vehicle headlamps can be used to mark the LZ. Parked at the edge of the cleared area, the vehicles should be between 20 and 25 metres apart, and angled at 45 degrees so that their headlights meet in the centre of the landing zone. The aircraft will approach them from behind, and come in between the vehicles, so they must not have radio aerials sticking up.

Night landing

To guide a helicopter onto the landing zone at night, lay out five lights in a 'T' shape pointing into the wind. Lights can be either lamps dug into the ground or torches pointing towards the direction the helicopter will be coming from. Put each light 10 paces apart.

wind direction

approach path

Vehicle-lit emergency night landing zone

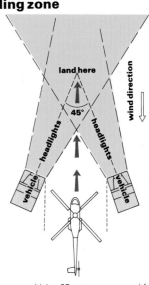

land here

45°

wind direction

headlights

vehicle

vehicle

Position two vehicles 25 metres apart and facing into the wind. Turn them slightly towards each other so that the intersection of their headlights forms an angle of 45 degrees. This will be the helicopter's landing point.

Troops must exit or enter the helicopter at incredible speed: in one operation in Angola, paratroopers had to clamber on board while under fire from a Cuban tank!

DEPLANING PROCEDURE

The troops must exit the helicopter as fast as possible, throwing packs out of the door and assuming an all-round defensive position. The two machine-gun (LMG) crews must exit first to provide covering fire for the rest of the stick. Normally the helicopter will land to emplane or deplane personnel but over long grass, bushes or uneven terrain, men and equipment are dropped while the helicopter hovers at between 1.2 and 1.8 m. In order to prevent the aircraft from rocking too much when the troops depart from a hovering helicopter they must not leap out sideways, but drop straight to the ground from the steps provided.

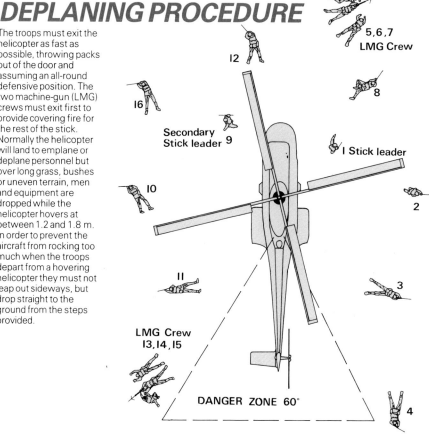

possible, the gunship should go in close to soften up the enemy with strafing fire before troops go in on the ground.

On the troop commander's signal, the transports will come down to prearranged positions in the LZ (landing zone). Where possible, they will touch down, but over rougher terrain such as long grass or badly broken ground they will stay in a low hover, one or two metres above the ground. Troops must be prepared to jump out, making sure they have all their equipment with them, and being careful not to upset the aircraft in the process – something that happens all too easily to a hovering helicopter. Unless they are in hot pursuit, with the enemy in sight, troops will make a defensive ring around the aircraft. Each trooper knows his position in the defensive structure, and goes to it without being told.

Trying to hide

Rather than try to run for it, insurgents may choose instead to go to ground, hoping to escape by hiding. This is especially true in open country. This means that pursuing forces have to be prepared to mount lengthy search operations whenever they are sent in to eliminate a guerrilla group. This causes a number of problems: it becomes necessary to re-supply with rations, to carry bedding and survival equipment and to have enough weaponry and ammunition for every conceivable circumstance.

In search and tracking operations, the fighting forces also need the help and support of specialists – especially intelligence officers and dogs and men trained in search and tracking techniques. The helicopter is the usual means of transport for these, to get the right people into the right

place in the shortest possible time.

As soon as the ground forces have been deployed from the aircraft, most of the helicopters will return to the nearest defended supply base, where they can be immediately refuelled and made ready to return to the combat zone. One or two craft will remain within a very short flight-time of the

ground forces, to be available to move troops from place to place within the combat zone if this becomes necessary.

The Rhodesians pioneered the Fire Force System, although their resources were very limited. This is an Alouette III spotting for a mortar shoot against an enemy position.

FLYING THE EAGLE PATROL

An RAF Puma swoops low over the countryside, keeping within 15 metres of the ground to avoid shoulder-launched anti-aircraft missiles. The Eagle Patrol will be landed to set up a surprise road block on an isolated road, which will catch the terrorists unawares.

5 points for a successful Eagle Patrol

1. Fly low to minimise the danger from ground fire.
2. Land out of sight of the target car so that it does not realise it will run into a road block.
3. Exit the helicopter quickly so that it can be airborne and away from the area as soon as possible.
4. As with any vehicle checkpoint, split your section so that at least two men check the vehicle, covered by at least two others.
5. Most cars you stop will be driven by innocent civilians, but you must maintain your concentration: if your attention wanders when a terrorist drives up to your roadblock, you will be in deep trouble.

copter. You can strike in any direction, you can deploy reserves quickly, you can cut the enemy off during a pursuit and you can carry out detailed air reconnaissance and observation.

Night flying

What is more, you can operate efficiently in a modern helicopter at night as well. You will need to fly at higher altitudes than by day to avoid obstructions, and usually some sort of landing aid is required, though this need only be in the form of a basic layout of lights.

Eagle patrols at night are difficult because of the random nature of landing sites, but they may be possible in good weather conditions using helicopter searchlights as a landing aid.

Eagle Patrols are the name given by the British Army to the technique used in an IS situation in which patrols are inserted by helicopter to mount a snap roadblock or ambush. They are usually in reaction to something the patrol commander has seen from the air himself or something that has happened within flying distance since the patrol has been airborne. In this sort of situation the helicopter gives the patrol the advantages of surprise, flexibility and speed of reaction.

Versatile deployment

Modern helicopters have a good radius of action and effective communications. Only very bad weather or exceptionally high terrain are likely to impede your movement in a heli-

Below: A section in Northern Ireland with a Wessex helicopter in the background. By inserting heli-borne troops into rural areas the Army makes it more difficult for terrorists to transport arms and ammunition.

HELICOPTERS AT WAR

For all their advantages, helicopters are intricate pieces of machinery. They are vulnerable to SAMs, small arms fire and artillery fire, especially when on the ground. The pilot himself is very vulnerable, and in operational areas he wears a nylon armoured vest and sits in an armoured seat.

Low and fast

The best way for a helicopter to avoid either small arms fire or SAMs is to fly low and fast. In Northern Ireland helicopters have remained remarkably immune – their tolerance to

Above: Many rural roads in Northern Ireland are so easily mined that road travel is prohibitively dangerous. Here, Army transport lies wrecked after command-detonated bombs caught several vehicles.

Above: Permanent Observation Posts near the border with the Irish Republic are usually supplied by air because of the danger of road travel.

Find Report
This should include:
1. The date and time of the find.
2. Location of find.
3. A detailed description of the hiding place.
4. A detailed description of what you have found.
5. Why you conducted the search.
6. Details of any arrests.
7. Any follow-up actions you have initiated.

Deployment
Time on the ground or in the hover must be kept to a minimum. Speed is essential; the patrol should be off the chopper and down in all-round defence in less than the time it takes a terrorist to get to a weapon, acquire a target and fire an aimed shot.

Vulnerability
Movement by air is a good deal safer than by road in the real bandit country of South Armagh, where PIRA have had considerable success with massive command-detonated land mines etc. Helicopters are themselves very vulnerable to ground fire; Wessex, Puma, and Lynx are not armoured and rely on the tactical flying skill of their pilots to avoid small arms fire.

Weapons
Be careful: they may be booby trapped. Do not clear them; contact an RUC or RMP Finds Team.

Action on a find
If you find anything suspicious, do not touch it. Think about the possibility of a covert operation (this may not be practicable), make sure the area is clear and secure it, keep everyone away from the scene, and, finally, tell your HQ.

EAGLE PATROL

Eagle patrols can react quickly to short-term intelligence and are ideal for snap vehicle check points, cordon and search operations and inserting the QRF (Quick Reaction Force). Helicopters provide commanders with immense flexibility and speed of reaction.

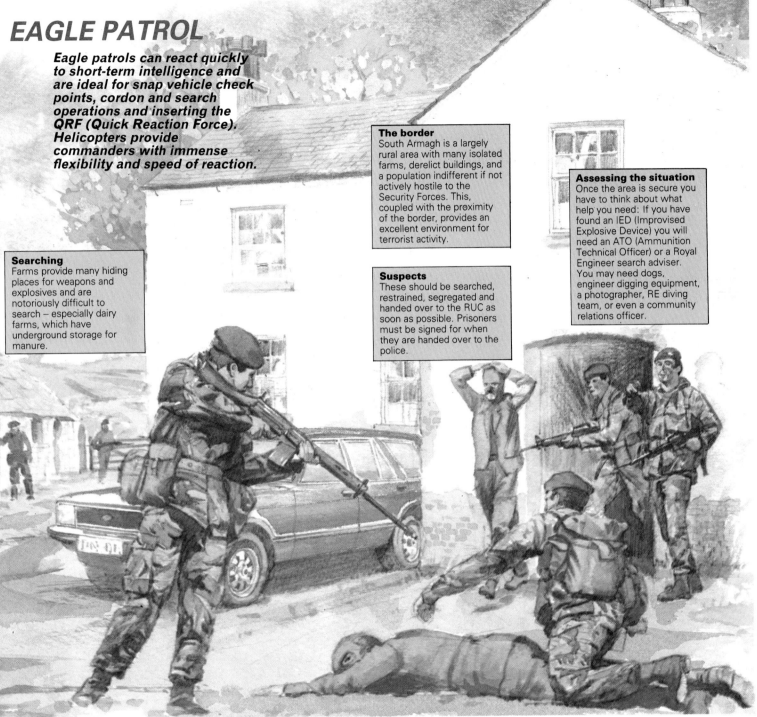

The border
South Armagh is a largely rural area with many isolated farms, derelict buildings, and a population indifferent if not actively hostile to the Security Forces. This, coupled with the proximity of the border, provides an excellent environment for terrorist activity.

Assessing the situation
Once the area is secure you have to think about what help you need: If you have found an IED (Improvised Explosive Device) you will need an ATO (Ammunition Technical Officer) or a Royal Engineer search adviser. You may need dogs, engineer digging equipment, a photographer, RE diving team, or even a community relations officer.

Searching
Farms provide many hiding places for weapons and explosives and are notoriously difficult to search – especially dairy farms, which have underground storage for manure.

Suspects
These should be searched, restrained, segregated and handed over to the RUC as soon as possible. Prisoners must be signed for when they are handed over to the police.

several hits is considerable.

Although some have been forced to land by damage caused by small arms fire, few have been 'shot down'. Where, however, terrorists or guerrillas have managed to obtain hand-held surface-to-air missile systems, such as the Soviet designed SA-7 'Grail', helicopters have been brought down; there is photographic evidence of successful engagements of Soviet helicopters in Afghanistan by the Mujahideen.

The counter to the SA-7 is to fly at 15 metres or less, so that the operator does not have sufficient time to acquire his target, fire the missile and achieve lock-on with the infra-red heat-seeking system during the brief exposure time of the target.

If you are going to operate with helicopters you must be familiar with the different types in use with the Army Air Corps and the RAF and you must understand their requirements. The Puma and the Wessex are the two helicopter types in the RAF that are most suitable for 'Eagle Patrols': they are twin-engined transport helicopters that are capable of carrying 12-16 fully armed and equipped troops. The Army Air Corps Lynx, though it only carries eight men, can also be used in this role. If you are operating with any of these types, you may be responsible for choosing a suitable landing site or LS for your helicopter. The ground should be reasonably even and solid if the helicopter is going to land rather than hover. All solid obstacles, loose

items and inflammable material must be cleared from the site: the term 'cleared to ground level' is used to indicate the requirement.

Airborne landing

If ground obstructions cannot be cleared, you can embark and disembark your patrol without the helicopter actually landing. However, your chosen LS should still offer as good an approach as possible and sufficient room for the pilot to manoeuvre on and around the LS. But because of the relatively high engine power required during hovering, loading and unloading is best carried out with the helicopter actually on the ground.

Obviously in an emergency situa-

HELICOPTERS AT WAR

A *GPMG* gunner gets into position to cover the rest of the patrol while they organise the 'snap' vehicle checkpoint. You must never forget all-round defence when on Internal Security operations.

tion, such as an urgent casualty evacuation, pilots are prepared to land or hover in far from ideal circumstances. The pilot will decide himself whether a landing is feasible.

Once you have met up with your helicopter you will then need to get your patrol on board. As patrol leader you should kneel by the door of the helicopter and count your patrol into the helicopter. Get in last and sit by the open door. That way you can see out and you will know where you are and what is going on.

Beware of the blades

Remember to brief everybody to crouch as they run in towards the helicopter, and nobody should move towards the helicopter until the pilot gives the 'thumbs up'. Windy conditions can make the rotors dip low and there have been terrible accidents with rotating helicopter blades decapitating unwary passengers.

Once the helicopter is airborne you will fly to your planned area of operations. It is then up to you and the helicopter pilot who will be talking to you over the intercom to select a likely tar-

If you are commanding an Eagle Patrol your place is in the doorway with the helicopter crewman. Count your men into the helicopter and enter last. Observe the ground below as you fly to the operational area.

get – probably a suspicious looking car on a lonely stretch of country road – and to swoop down ahead of it and mount an instant vehicle check.

The trick is to use the contours so that your suspect does not see you landing ahead of him; in that way he will suddenly round a bend and find a snap roadblock where he least expects it. Your helicopter will drop you and then immediately take off and loiter somewhere safe rather than present a static target on the ground. As soon as you have carried out your check you can recall the helicopter on the radio, resume your patrol and repeat the process somewhere else.

Your tasks on the ground need not be confined to mounting snap vehicle checkpoints. You may be dropped in a particular location to mount an ambush or act as a cut-off party in a larger operation. Once you are on the ground the same rules apply for your roadblock as if you were operating in a vehicle or foot patrol.

Instant tracking

The great advantage of mounting a roadblock from a helicopter is, if someone does evade or crash through your roadblock the helicopter will be instantly available to track the car.

Once you have carried out your vehicle check you can call in your helicopter and move on to the next task. If sufficient helicopters are available Eagle Patrols are a cost-effective and efficient method of dominating a large rural area with limited resources. If you carry out an Eagle Patrol in bandit country, remember the rules associated with working with helicopters: keep your wits about you, and remember that the car you decide to stop and check from the air may be carrying terrorists.

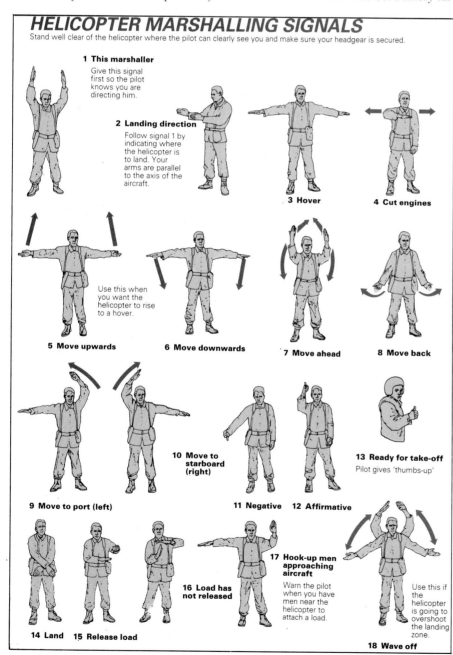

HELICOPTER MARSHALLING SIGNALS

Stand well clear of the helicopter where the pilot can clearly see you and make sure your headgear is secured.

1 This marshaller
Give this signal first so the pilot knows you are directing him.

2 Landing direction
Follow signal 1 by indicating where the helicopter is to land. Your arms are parallel to the axis of the aircraft.

3 Hover

4 Cut engines

5 Move upwards
Use this when you want the helicopter to rise to a hover.

6 Move downwards

7 Move ahead

8 Move back

9 Move to port (left)

10 Move to starboard (right)

11 Negative

12 Affirmative

13 Ready for take-off
Pilot gives 'thumbs-up'

14 Land

15 Release load

16 Load has not released

17 Hook-up men approaching aircraft
Warn the pilot when you have men near the helicopter to attach a load.

18 Wave off
Use this if the helicopter is going to overshoot the landing zone.

5 AIRBORNE BRIGADE

Two battalions of paratroopers provide the brigade spearhead. They can operate as regular light infantry, as air assault troops or in the airborne role.

5 Airborne Brigade is not one of Britain's famous regiments. It does not have centuries of history to its name, and it has no colours with honours carried proudly to mark battles gloriously won or heroically lost. Yet the brigade is one of the elite formations of the British Army. It is a fighting unit which is the heart of Britain's rapid intervention capability, and it will lead NATO's rapid reaction force in the 1990s.

British airborne forces were founded during World War II. In two short years they grew from a small cadre of parachutists into division-sized formations able to make up an

5 Airborne Brigade includes an Army Air Corps squadron of Lynxes and Gazelles, together with a light armoured regiment equipped with Scorpion and Scimitar tracked reconnaissance vehicles.

entire airborne army. However, such enormous growth was to prove short-lived. The end of the war saw a massive reduction in the armed forces of all combatants, and Britain's parachute forces shrank dramatically.

The end of the empire and the dedication of the British Army to NATO meant that by the 1970s the Parachute Regiment had shrunk to a three-battalion ghost of its former self. Airborne training was continued almost as a matter of tradition rather than need,

since the regiment's role was to fight as conventional light infantry, primarily in defence of the British Isles. In any case, the Royal Air Force did not have or was not willing to allocate the transport assets necessary to support a major airborne operation. The days of 'out-of-area' operations were considered to be long past. Then came the Argentine invasion of the Falklands. Two parachute battalions were attached to 3 Commando Brigade and distinguished themselves in the war that followed.

Falklands war

Clearly, the Falklands war was an aberration, but just as clearly it showed that there was a place for a British rapid intervention force, ready at short notice for operations outside the NATO area. 5 Infantry Brigade, which had also taken part in the Falklands campaign, was chosen to fill the role, and with the change in task and structure it became 5 Airborne Brigade.

The brigade consists of two parachute battalions, two infantry battalions trained in the air assault role, an artillery regiment and a light armoured regiment. It also has under its command such vital support units as an engineer regiment, a field ambulance, and a logistic battalion consisting of a REME field workshop, an ordnance company and a transport squadron. Many of the support units are also parachute-qualified. Immediate air support is provided by an Army Air Corps squadron equipped with Lynx and Gazelle helicopters, but if large-scale movement is required the brigade can call on the much larger Chinooks and Pumas of the Royal Air Force.

Every piece of equipment in the brigade is air-portable in the RAF's C-130 Hercules aircraft. These fly out to the theatre of operations, establishing an airhead from which the fighting units will move onto the objective. Troops can be parachuted in, or helicopters can be used to mount an air assault. In certain circumstances the brigade can carry out a tactical air-landing operation, flying directly into action in the C-130s.

Airborne operation

In an airborne operation the first people in will be the Pathfinder Platoon, using HALO techniques to make clandestine landings 12 to 24 hours ahead of the main assault. They make a reconnaissance of the drop zone. The LPBG, or Lead Parachute Battalion Group, will follow, accompanied by the brigade staff together with a light artillery battery and a number of vehicles. Flown in on 21 C-130s, the LPBG will jump at low level, all troops being on the ground within four minutes. The LPBG's task is to suppress local opposition and establish an airhead so that reinforcements and equipment can be flown in.

While the LPBG is setting up the airhead, the Follow-Up Parachute Battalion Group, or FUPBG, either jumps or is flown in. With two battalions on the ground it is now possible to move out towards the objective, while the follow-on infantry battalion groups and the heavy equipment are flown in to the airhead. The heavy equipment includes the remainder of the artillery as well as Scorpion light tanks and Fox armoured cars.

5 Airborne Brigade is based at Aldershot in the south of England, and is theoretically at five days' notice for out-of-area operations. In fact, the brigade reckons it can be up and running at much shorter notice. It is a lightly armed, lightly equipped formation designed to perform swift 'smash and grab' missions, and is expected to operate on its own without major support. The brigade will rely upon surprise to achieve success.

While it is possible that the brigade might be used as the spearhead of a British force in war, as happened in the Falklands, it is more likely to be used in an evacuation or a rescue mission. British nationals are working in large numbers all round the world, and each one is a potential hostage. In the best case operations, 5 Airborne Brigade would be used to organise or supervise an evacuation, while the worst case scenario would see elements of the brigade fighting its way into hostile territory, rescuing hostages and getting them safely out of the country.

Because of the brigade's unique role, it operates some equipment which is rare in the rest of the army. The Supacat all-terrain vehicle is not amphibious, but it can ford streams almost a metre deep. It is equally at home on sand or in mud, and can handle up to 30 cm of snow.

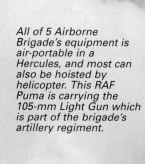

All of 5 Airborne Brigade's equipment is air-portable in a Hercules, and most can also be hoisted by helicopter. This RAF Puma is carrying the 105-mm Light Gun which is part of the brigade's artillery regiment.

A French army Alouette III helicopter carries four AS.11 wire-guided anti-tank missiles. The French pioneered the use of military helicopters in Algeria and were the first to add anti-tank weapons to their helicopters.

SS.11 WIRE-GUIDED MISSILE

The French were among the pioneers of anti-tank missile warfare with the development by Nord Aviation – now part of Aérospatiale – of their SS.10/ SS.11 series of missiles. They were the first to turn the helicopter into an anti-tank weapon, by mounting their missiles onto the turbine-powered Sud-Aviation Alouette II light helicopters.

Development of the Aérospatiale SS.10 began as early as 1953, when the Nord Type 5210 was put onto the drawing board. Better performance and range was to lead to the similar SS.11. Development was rapid, and the missile entered service with the French army in 1956.

Line-of-sight weapon

The SS.11 was a manually-guided line-of-sight weapon. The operator acquired his target through the sight and then launched the missile along that line-of-sight. The outgoing missile had a bright flare in its tail, which allowed the operator to spot it easily

through his sight, even at distances of three kilometres. He then flew the missile towards its target with a joystick control, sending flight corrections to the missile along wires.

None of this seems surprising today. After all, most anti-tank missiles currently in service operate in a similar or more advanced fashion. But when the SS.11 was new, more than 30 years ago, this was a revelation. The first missiles were designed to operate from the ground, either launched from a tripod or from a vehicle. However, the French army quickly realised that it might be possible to fire the missile from the air. Not from a conventional aircraft, however: it would be next to impossible to fire a wire-guided missile from a high-speed platform, although they thought a hovering or slow-moving helicopter might prove effective.

At first results with the air-launched AS.11 were hard to come by. It was not easy to steer the missile accurately: the operator tended to

overcorrect and many found it hard to co-ordinate steering in both the lateral and vertical planes. From 1962, however, a modified version of the SS.11 was produced. This was the SS.11B1, which made use of transistorised electronic systems in place of the older valves. Transistorisation reduced weight and increased reliability and the ability to withstand rough handling.

Different warheads

SS.11s have been fitted with a variety of warheads over the years. The standard anti-armour one was the Type 140AC, with a HEAT shaped-charge warhead. The Type 140AP02 was designed for more lightly armoured or troop-carrying targets and had a semi-armour-piercing delayed-action anti-personnel warhead. There was also a warhead designed for use against personnel and soft targets, the Type 140AP59, fitted with a high-explosive fragmentation charge.

The problem with air-launched variants of the SS.11 was that it was very difficult to hit a target. It was hard to get accurate results when operating from a small, vibrating helicopter, especially with a distorted view through curved Plexiglas panels. The breakthrough came with the development, in the early 1960s, of TCA, or Télé Command Automatique. Now known as Semi-Automatic Command-to-Line-of-Sight and the standard means of controlling medium and small anti-armour weapons, the operator was absolved of any need to fly the weapon. All he had to do was to keep the sight on the target and the missile automatically flew along the centre of a parallel line defined by an infra-red sensing system.

Semi-automatic

A modified SS.11 with a much improved semi-automatic guidance system entered service in the late 1960s. Known as Harpoon, it was produced in some numbers for use by the French, West German and Saudi Arabian armies. With a range of 3000 metres, the SS.11 could penetrate over 600 mm of rolled homogeneous armour plate. The missile weighed 30 kilograms, was 1.22 metres long and had a wing span of 50 cm.

In the 1970s a new missile based on the SS.11 was introduced. The SS.12 and its air-launched equivalent AS.12 could be fired by SS.11 and AS.11 launchers, but the larger missiles were twice as heavy, with double the range and a warhead with more than four times the power.

SS.11s have been used in combat several times, especially during the brushfire wars of the 1970s. They were used by both sides during the Iran-Iraq War of the 1980s, and may have been fired unsuccessfully by the Iraqis during the Gulf War of 1991. Although already obsolescent, SS.11s were fired by British Wasp helicopters against Argentine ground positions during the Falklands war of 1982. A Naval Wasp also used an AS.12 missile to damage the Argentine submarine *Santa Fe* during the retaking of South Georgia.

Final production

The SS.11 family was a highly successful product. By the early 1980s, when the missile finally went out of production, nearly 200,000 missiles had been produced, including some 10,000 of the larger SS.12 and AS.12 missiles. SS.11s were sold to the armies of more than 30 countries, including Argentina, France, India, Iran, Iraq, Italy, Spain, Tunisia, Turkey and the United Kingdom.

Above: An Alouette III launches an AS.11 missile: note the modest launch signature and the flare in the tail that helps the gunner gather the missile into his sight and steer it into the target. The helicopter cannot attempt any hard manoeuvring while the missile is in flight or the gunner will miss.

Below: A Royal Navy Westland Wasp launches an AS.11, providing a clear view of the missile. Wasps damaged the Argentine submarine Santa Fe off Grytviken harbour in South Georgia in 1982 after depth charge explosions dissuaded the Argentines from submerging. With its conning tower penetrated, the submarine was forced to surrender.

EYEWITNESS

G-cars and K-cars were the names for the French-built Alouette helicopters used by Rhodesian forces for transport and escort duties.

RHODESIAN RAIDERS

A former member of the Rhodesian Light Infantry tells the story of a 'Fire Force' mission during the Rhodesian War.

"In the early afternoon of 7 March 1979 I was one of 12 men from the RLI's Support Commando called out for the second time to an area near Gwanda, in southern Rhodesia. Following a short flight, our three G-cars began to orbit a group of neat fields, flanked by craggy hills on one side and a small wooded area on the other. Before long it was decided to deploy callsign Stop-1 on their own, and to insert Stop-2 and -3 at the base of a rocky gomo (hill) on the edge of a mealie (corn) field.

"While a K-car provided overhead cover, Corporal M. Robie's Stop-3 was put down, only to find itself involved in a firefight almost immediately; our G-car was forced to remain aloft while the K-car dealt with it, and we were then ordered to go in and reinforce Stop-3. As we banked to begin our descent we came under automatic fire from another terrorist, but the Alouette simply levelled out and

Below: Members of a 1 RLI patrol wait to be flown on a Fire Force mission. By this time, late in the war, the RLI was one of the most combat-effective units in the Rhodesian army.

thudded in to land opposite a treeline now occupied by Stop-3. We leapt out and doubled through the swirling cloud of red dust thrown up by the helicopter's rotors, to be met by two of Robie's men who were dragging along a terrorist killed by the K-car. The body was unceremoniously flung aboard the Alouette for transportation back to base, where it would later be photographed and fingerprinted by Special Branch.

"As the chopper departed with its gruesome cargo, I positioned myself behind the negligible cover of a scrawny tree just as one of our troopers, Nick Webster, and Stop-2's gunner, Micky Maitland, both opened up. Everyone else joined in. The main target appeared to be a tree about 70 metres to our front-right, but Webster and Maitland were concentrating their fire against the mealie crop in the middle of the field, well away from the tree!

Under attack

"Then from out of the confusion came a voice of command: Corporal Robie yelled at us to stand up and follow him into the open towards the bullet-riddled tree. Heart pumping wildly, I followed the others in the dash across the carefully ploughed field. Immediately the earth to our front erupted in little puffs of dirt, but due to the sounds of our own weapons it was impossible to determine just by listening who was shooting at us.

"Somehow we reached our objective unscathed. Stop-3 threw themselves behind some rocks but I and the rest of Stop-2 were forced to lie in the open, between the rocks on our right and the rows of corn off to our left.

"Although Corporal Robie had assumed command he was in fact outranked by Lieutenant Williams, a young subaltern who had joined the Commando just five days previously.

An RLI machine-gunner fires his FN MAG into possible terrorist hiding places during a Fire Force sweep through the bush.

To our horror, he now ordered Stop-2 further out into the clearing. I relayed the officer's order to Nick on my left: 'Lieutenant Williams says you blokes are to spread out towards the mealie field!'

'You too, Terrell!' shouted Lieutenant Williams.

'Bollocks!' Webster screamed back.

'What did he say?' demanded Williams.

'They're not too keen on the idea, sir.'

'There's a bloody terrorist in that mealie field with an RPD, for Christ's sake! Tell him that!'

'Sir, there's a terrorist with a machine-gun in the mealie field!'

'Who says so?'

'Webster, sir. He saw him.'

'Rubbish! Spread out!'

"Thankfully for us, the argument was never resolved, because Corporal Robie threw a WP grenade at the tree, believing that it still concealed our terrorist. It thudded into the tree trunk and promptly bounced back to land smack in the middle of our little group. There was a sudden silence as we all stared at the green canister before burying our faces in the dry earth. A second later the grenade detonated in a dazzling display of blazing phosphorus. Remarkably, no-one was hurt!

"Then we began a typical bush-clearance operation, climbing over the gomo, nervously firing into the dense undergrowth and tossing grenades into caves, never knowing where the enemy might choose to hide. Suddenly Lance Corporal Graham Gilbert shouted 'Check, check, check!'

"I was just in time to 'check' two figures armed with AKs who had broken cover a hundred metres to our front. We all opened up simultaneously, six FN rifles and two MAGs sending a hail of deadly fire towards the unfortunate terrorists, who quickly dived headlong into some long grass.

"As we ran forward, Corporal Robie directed a G-car towards the enemy position. We all watched as the Alouette hovered 10 feet above the bush, firing twin-Brownings into the thicket. He ceased firing and cautiously approached the spot and spread out in order to search for the floppies.

"I dreaded this part of a sweep. Was he dead, or could he still be alive, perhaps even peering down the sights of his weapon at this very moment? Levelling my rifle, I peered through the leafy branches. Suddenly from the other side of the bush there came a yell, instantly followed by several rounds which burst through the thicket, narrowly missing me.

"I ducked down, screaming 'Hold your fire! Hold your fire!' The shooting abruptly stopped and an anxious Lance Corporal Gilbert appeared.

"It was quite ridiculous. The tension was relieved a moment later when someone pulled a body from beneath the bush. It was the other terrorist, his face smashed from the G-car's burst of fire.

"We dumped the bodies together in a clearing and waited for the G-cars. Idly, I pulled up a trouser leg to scratch an itch. Glancing down, I saw that my leg above my jump-boot was covered with tiny black parasites: cattle ticks! Looking around, I noticed that the ground we were sitting on was crawling with them ... and now so were we!"

Helicopters gave the RLI the mobility needed to hunt down an elusive enemy in thick brush, miles away from the nearest roads.

SIKORSKY
HAWKS

For the non-specialised press, helicopters generally lack the 'stealthy', 'sexy', or 'smart' characteristics deemed necessary to sell papers and fill television programmes. Yet Sikorsky Black Hawks and Seahawks undoubtedly were among the unsung technological heroes of the Gulf War. What they lacked in 'press appeal' they more than made up for in reliability and adaptability while transporting troops and ammunition, inserting special forces, searching for and rescuing allied personnel, taking boarding parties to blockade runners and keeping the sea-lanes open.

In October 1965, 26 months after the UH-1D (the first version of the ubiquitous 'Huey' capable of carrying squad-sized units) had entered service and 23 months before the UH-1H (the numerically most important variant) started coming off the assembly line, the US Army obtained approval from the Department of Defense for its Qualitative Material Development Objective spelling out its requirement for a 'Huey' successor. However, vast expenditures incurred during the Vietnam War and the need to provide a steady supply of helicopters to front-line units combined to delay the issue of a request for proposal (RFP) for the Utility Tactical Transport Aircraft System (UTTAS) helicopter for over six years. Finally, the RFP was issued in January 1972. It called for a heli-

copter which could carry squad-sized units, like the UH-1D and UH-1H, but was also capable of doing so in high temperatures and/or at high altitude (conditions under which both 'Huey' versions were found to be grossly underpowered and unable to carry their design load). The new utility helicopter was also required to be highly manoeuvrable, more reliable and more easily maintained. Key performance requirements included a cruising speed of 269-324 km/h, an endurance of 2.3 hours at that speed and an initial climb rate of 2.3-2.8 m/sec.

Proposals were submitted by Bell (for its Model 240), Boeing-Vertol (for its Model 179) and Sikorsky (for its S-70) on 27 March 1972. Five months later, after rejecting the Bell 240, which was found to be wanting in terms of new technology, the Army announced that Boeing and Sikorsky should each build a ground test vehicle and three prototypes of their YUH-61A and YUH-60A for competitive evaluation. Both were to be

The UH-60 Black Hawk is a versatile helicopter, far more capable than the well known UH-1 'Huey' of the Vietnam era.

powered by a pair of General Electric YT-700-GE-700 engines, have a new turboshaft, which had just won an Army-sponsored competition, and were to commence trials before the end of November 1974. The first YUH-60A (Sikorsky S-70) did so with time to spare on 17 October 1974, whereas the first YUH-61A (Boeing-Vertol Model 179) just made it on 29 November 1974.

The US Army took delivery of the three YUH-60As and three YUH-61As during ceremonies at Fort Benning, Georgia, on 20 March 1976. One of each was sent to Edwards AFB, California, for testing by the Army's Aviation Engineering Flight Activity, and the others initially went to Fort Rucker, Alabama, for testing under tactical conditions. Subsequently, YUH-60As and YUH-61s went to Eglin AFB, Florida, for climatic testing

UH-60 Black Hawks in Saudi Arabia during the early days of the US military deployment to the Gulf. The helicopter's performance in the hot, dusty climate exceeded expectations.

Rotor strength
The rotors of the UH-60 are designed to survive hits from machine-gun and light cannon rounds.

Defensive weapons
In its normal troop-carrying role the UH-60 is fitted with machine-guns only, but a significant proportion of the newer models will be able to double as anti-tank/assault helicopters.

Troop capacity
Able to carry a fully-equipped squad, the Black Hawk is roomy enough to accommodate up to 20 men in light order.

Above: The Black Hawk can carry up to 20 lightly-equipped soldiers. However, the normal combat load is a three-man crew and 11 fully-equipped infantrymen.

Left: The UH-60L introduced shoulder-mounted fuselage-braced wings, which can carry either extra fuel tanks or weapons. In 1991 the UH-60 completed a three-year programme qualifying it to fire Hellfire anti-tank missiles.

in a climatic hangar; to Fort Irwin, California, and Fort Richardson, Alaska, for evaluation under desert and Arctic conditions; and to Campbell, Kentucky, for more operational testing, including night operations.

As the result of a mishap during a flight on the night of 9 August 1975, when an Army pilot made a crash-landing in a heavily-wooded area at Fort Campbell, Sikorsky was able to demonstrate that its YUH-60A more than met the Army's requirements for improved crash-worthiness. Two days later, after the area around the crashed helicopter was cleared and its main and tail blades were replaced, the YUH-60A was flown out of the site. After additional checks were made at the main base, the aircraft was returned to unrestricted service.

On 23 December 1976, at the end of this eight-month period of Government Competitive Testing, the Department of Defense announced that the Army had selected the Sikorsky UH-60A as the winner of its UTTAS competition.

The first production Black Hawk flew on 17 October 1978. The selection of the name Black Hawk does not follow the Army's tradition of naming its aircraft after Indian tribes, as Black Hawk is not the name of a tribe but is

UH-60 Black Hawk

The US Army now operates a total of 1,400 Black Hawks in a wide variety of roles, from troop and cargo transport to special forces operations behind enemy lines. The Black Hawk has achieved significant success on the export market and also serves as a naval helicopter.

Heat exhaust
Different models of the Black Hawk have introduced new systems to reduce the heat emissions and make the helicopter less of a target for heat-seeking missiles.

that of the leader of the Fox and Sauk Indians during the Black Hawk War in 1832.

Deliveries to the US Army began on 31 October 1978 and, following service trials and initial training of crews at Fort Rucker, Alabama, and maintenance personnel at Fort Eustis, Virginia, UH-60As entered service with the 101st Airborne Division (Air Assault) in June 1979, when four aircraft were delivered for Force Development Test and Experimentation at Fort Campbell, Kentucky.

Combat load

Although nominally carrying the same design load (a crew of three and 11 combat-equipped troops) as the UH-1H, the UH-60A can accommodate 20 lightly-equipped troops and carry heavier external loads (3630 kilograms versus 2000 kilograms) than the type it was designed to replace. Moreover, the UH-60A quickly proved to be a far more capable combat helicopter than the UH-1H, as it has enhanced crash and enemy fire survivability. It also has much better overall performance, particularly under 'hot-and-high' conditions.

With the addition of External Stores Support System (ESSS) shoulder-mounted/fuselage-braced wings to carry either fuel tanks or weapons, the fitting of a Hover Infra-Red Suppressor Subsystem (HIRSS) to cool engine exhaust and reduce infra-red detectability, the arrival of the more powerful UH-60L variant and the installation of upgraded counter measures systems, the Black Hawk has evolved into the world's leading utility helicopter. Combat-proven in Grenada during Operation Urgent Fury in October 1983 and in Panama during Operation Just Cause in December 1989, the Black Hawk achieved conspicuous successes during the Gulf War. It confounded the critics who thought that it would be difficult to maintain under desert conditions, and the mission capable rate – which had been around the 75 per cent rate prior to the start of combat operations – rose to above 85 per cent once the fighting started. Moreover, the Black Hawk has achieved significant success on the export market in spite of the availability of cheaper, but less capable, utility helicopters, and it has hatched a family of derivatives for a variety of military and naval applications. Even more remarkable is the fact that these derivatives have in turn set standards which remain unmatched in their fields.

A flight of Hawks

UH-60A derivatives have been proposed or built for the US Army to fulfil a variety of roles, including the original assault transport mission

Supporting US troops from Panama to the Gulf War, the Black Hawk has proved a major success for Sikorsky with over 1,600 helicopters delivered so far.

(UH-60A with ESSS stub wings, UH-60A Enhanced with upgraded self-defence armament and passive defensive systems, UH-60L, UH-60M, UH-60I), electronic warfare (EH-60A,

Right: The SH-60B is the US Navy's latest anti-submarine helicopter. Lack of rocket or gun armament forced the Navy to call in Army or Royal Navy helicopters to engage Iraqi light craft in the Gulf.

YEH-60B and EH-60C) and special operations (MH-60A. MH-60L and MH-60K).

Naval derivatives

Naval derivatives of the UH-60A include LAMPS/ASW variants and search and rescue versions (HH-60H for the USN and HH-60J for the USCG): all of these have received special anti-corrosion treatment for extended operations at sea. In the LAMPS (Light Airborne Multi-Purpose System) role. the SH-60B has greatly increased US Navy anti-submarine warfare capability. It carries two ASW torpedoes and 25 sonobuoys, and has expanded sensor capability. computer-based data handling and analysis and increased ship/air tactical integration via a directional data-link. However, the Seahawk cannot operate from smaller ships and therefore must be regarded as complementing rather than replacing the Kaman SH-2F Seasprite in the LAMPS role.

Specialised Hawks

UH-60 derivatives have also been developed for the USAF for use in the combat/search and rescue and special operations roles. In these roles. the HH/MH-60 variants have been found to be somewhat wanting, as have their naval counterparts (HH-60F and HH-60J). when compared with the

helicopters they replaced. Although their performance and reliability are far superior to those of the older machines. with their pilots being quick to praise their ample power reserve which greatly eases refuelling from tanker-configured HC/MC-130s. the HH/MH-60s have a much smaller internal volume (particularly when auxiliary tanks are fitted in the cabin) and are unable to land on water. Para-rescue personnel prefer the old Pelicans. Jolly Greens and Super Jollies to the Jayhawks and Pave Hawks. as their low cabin ceiling makes suiting-up more difficult and long flights to the rescue more tiring.

The future of the Sikorsky Hawk series appears to be secure for several

years, with the US Army, the US Air Force and the US Navy, respectively. having formulated procurement plans for 168 UH-60Ls and MH-60Ks. 20 MH-60G/HH-60Gs. 88 SH-60B/Fs and HH-60Hs during 1991-1993. while the Japanese Maritime Self-Defence Force will order 36 additional SH-60Js as part of the Japanese Mid-term Defence Build-up Programme (1991-1995). Additional export orders are also likely to materialise. and by 31 March 1992 Sikorsky had delivered some 1.600 H-60/S-70s.

The UH-60 Black Hawk achieved a 75-85 per cent mission capable rate in the Gulf. The US Army will take delivery of another 60 UH-60s per year until 1996 and has an option on another 180 in 1997-99.

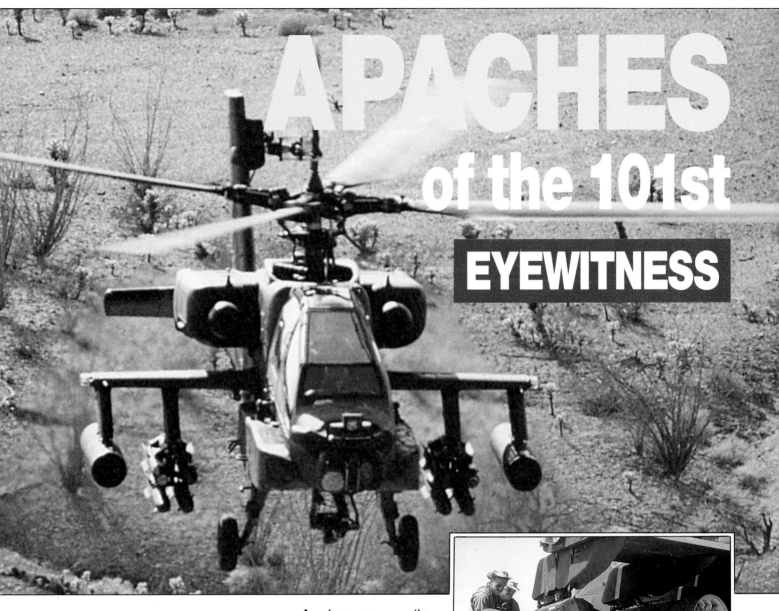

APACHES of the 101st

EYEWITNESS

Lieutenant Colonel William Bryan commanded an AH-64 Apache battalion of the 229th Aviation Regiment, attached to the US Army's 101st Air Assault Division, during the Gulf War.

"We knew that on G-day, the day the ground war started, the division was going to establish an airhead very deep inside Iraq. So in the week before that my mission was reconnaissance, to check the route into the country, destroy fortifications and clear the zone of enemy forces. The 101st's sector was 50k wide and 200k deep. On G-day, the division moved along pre-selected air routes to an operating base 150k into Iraq. We had troops on the ground and the forward base up and running within eight hours.

"When we came across a convoy, I would attack with one of the battalion's three companies. As the attack progressed I had one company attacking, one about 30k back in a holding area, and one 50k back at the FAARP – the forward area re-arming and refuelling point – at the division's forward operating base. There might only have

Apaches were among the first coalition assets deployed to the Gulf, flown disassembled in C-5 Galaxy cargo planes. Assembled, armed and flying within two days, their task was to stop Saddam Hussein's tanks should an attack on Saudi Arabia follow the invasion of Kuwait.

been a third of our people up there, but the enemy was being engaged continuously. If you really want to pile them all in you can, but then there's going to be a break in the action when everybody goes back to re-arm and refuel.

Nowhere to hide

"Companies normally operate in two teams. The light team of two Apaches will usually be the first to engage, covered by the heavy team of three or four helicopters. Then the heavy team will take up the fight. In Europe we're taught to mask, to use the terrain as cover from behind which we launch attacks. In the desert, you couldn't hide. It should

have been extremely dangerous since some of their anti-aircraft missile systems outranged us, but the Iraqis showed little or no desire to fight. They had the equipment but they didn't have the resolve.

"Had the Iraqis been an armoured force we would have made stand-off attacks, but in this case we shot them with 30-mm cannon fire to get them stopped and the people dismounted. Then we fired three Hellfires, which took out the three lead vehicles. From that point on we were able to finish them off with 30-mm and 2.75-in rockets.

"We never got into a real tank battle. On the fourth day of the ground war we did do a classic deep attack, moving about 300 kilometres towards Basra and intercepting one of the Republican Guard divisions as it attempted to withdraw north across the Euphrates. We used the same movement technique: attacking in three companies, but each company attacked in line, five abreast, rather than as two teams. By that time there were so many oil-well fires and vehicles burning that it was almost dark even though it was mid-afternoon. We had to use our FLIR – forward-looking infra-red – sensors to see the targets, and even those were blanked out by smoke at 3000 metres. We called it 'Hell's half-acre'. You could only see about 300 metres with the naked eye.

"There were hundreds of vehicles in the column. This time we were fired on; we were engaged by several heat-

Below: Apaches of the 101st sit on the ground deep inside Iraq. The division's FAARP – the forward area re-arming and refuelling point – is the helicopter force's forward operating base, from where they would strike at Iraqi armour up to 100 kilometres ahead of the division's ground troops.

seeking missiles and we think that some radar-guided SAM-6s were fired. It was like an inferno: there were so many fires and so much smoke that none of the enemy systems could acquire us. Most of what we fired at we hit, however. Visually, you could just see the flash of the explosions going off in the tunnel-like darkness, but through the FLIR the intense heat created by burning vehicles was easily visible.

Adverse conditions

"There has been a lot of controversy about the Apache. We lived with that aircraft through sandstorms, moisture – we had 10 in of rain in January – and extreme heat, yet the aircraft continued to operate with more than 90 per cent serviceability. There was no other platform in the Gulf that could fly so low, or could enagage such an array of targets with pinpoint accuracy, whatever the weather or the time of day or night. It was one of the few pieces of equipment that could move 300 kilometres in a matter of hours, engage a major enemy force and return. Most important, however, it was manned and maintained by highly motivated and proud people. We've come a long way in the 20 years since Vietnam, and the calibre of the American soldier is probably the best we've ever had. If you take these type of people and give them this type of high technology equipment, you're practically unbeatable."

Below: Agile and lethal, the Apache was one of the most effective destroyers of Iraqi armour and vehicles. Operating with the forward ground troops, it could also get into action more frequently than fixed-wing aircraft.

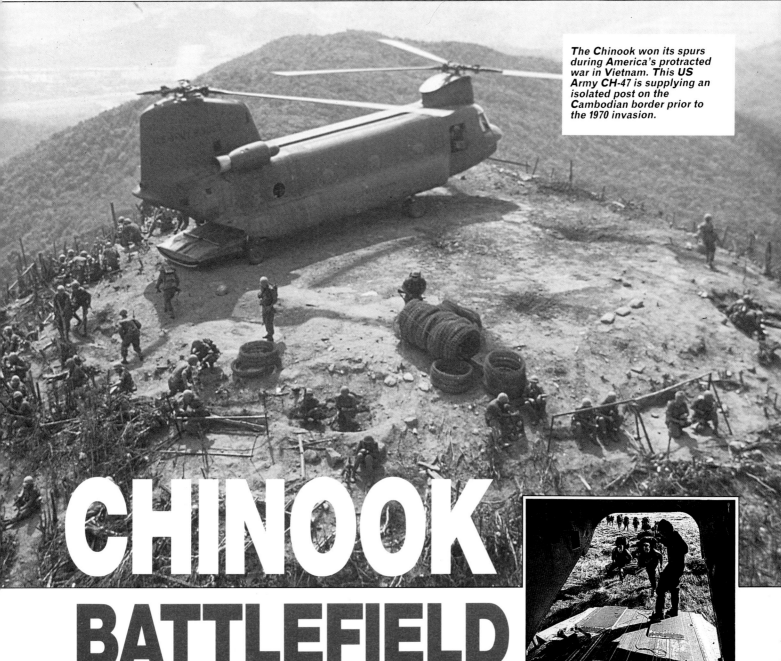

The Chinook won its spurs during America's protracted war in Vietnam. This US Army CH-47 is supplying an isolated post on the Cambodian border prior to the 1970 invasion.

CHINOOK
BATTLEFIELD
BIG LIFTER

Troops run up the broad rear cargo ramp of a CH-47. The big twin-rotor helicopter is equally capable of performing assault, transport and flying-crane missions.

2 June 1982, the Falkland Islands. A recce by Army Scout helicopters revealed that the Argies had vacated Fitzroy, a strategically placed settlement only 15 miles from Port Stanley. It was imperative that we seize it before they could return. The paras could yomp there, but that would have taken all night, and moving the required bayonet strength up by Scout or even Sea King helicopter would have required too many shuttles backwards and forwards, taking almost as long.

The RAF's only Chinook on the Islands, one of four to escape the sinking of the *Atlantic Conveyor*, came to the rescue. Officially the RAF's Chinooks have seats for 44 troops, but the Chinook can lift 12 tons, so when carrying men the problem is bulk, not weight. Desperate situations call for desperate measures, so they jammed in 81 standing paras and flew them to Fitzroy, then turned around and flew in another 75. The RAF loadmaster folded the seats away and the troops had to stand, jammed together like sardines. It was worse than a tube train in the rush hour, but it got the job done efficiently in double-quick time, and that's what the Chinook is all about.

Again and again in the Falklands the Chinook proved itself capable of tackling the jobs that no other helicopter could do, from recovering unserviceable Sea King helicopters to lifting 64 casualties at a time or shifting huge quantities of ammunition. While most helicopters regard a single underslung 105-mm gun as a big load, it was routine for the Chinook to carry three: two inside the spacious cabin, and one slung beneath. Perhaps the most remarkable thing about Chinook operations in the Falklands was that the aircraft just kept on flying, even though all the spares, tools and servicing equipment had been lost when the *Atlantic Conveyor* went down. As

Inside the Chinook

well as being incredibly versatile, the Chinook is very tough.

The Boeing Vertol CH-47 Chinook, to give it its full title, has been in production since 1961, but the basic aircraft has been dramatically improved since then, with uprated engines and transmission giving radically improved performance and lifting capability. New avionics and systems are being developed all the time, and the latest Chinook variant is a very sophisticated machine designed for Special Forces insertion missions at night or in foul weather. This aircraft, the MH-47D, even has a jousting lance-like, inflight-refuelling probe to extend its range, allowing it to operate far behind enemy lines.

Formidable reputation

The Chinook built itself a formidable reputation during the Vietnam War. By late 1972, when the US was beginning its withdrawal from the region, 550 of the 684 Chinooks built up to that time had served in the war, flying over 750,000 hours and airlifting 11,500 damaged or downed US aircraft to safety. Only about 170 were lost in action, although others were transferred to the South Vietnamese air force and were subsequently captured, and used, by the North Vietnamese. The initial Chinook variant, the CH-47A, could lift a load of

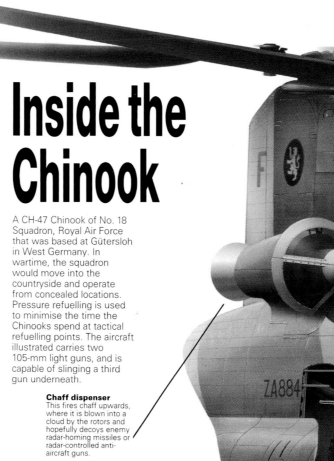

A CH-47 Chinook of No. 18 Squadron, Royal Air Force that was based at Gütersloh in West Germany. In wartime, the squadron would move into the countryside and operate from concealed locations. Pressure refuelling is used to minimise the time the Chinooks spend at tactical refuelling points. The aircraft illustrated carries two 105-mm light guns, and is capable of slinging a third gun underneath.

Chaff dispenser
This fires chaff upwards, where it is blown into a cloud by the rotors and hopefully decoys enemy radar-homing missiles or radar-controlled anti-aircraft guns.

Tail ramp
The tail ramp is hydraulically powered with a retractable tongue and can be left partially or fully open or even removed entirely if you are cramming in an extra-long cargo.

No. 78 Squadron Chinooks based at Mount Pleasant make their way across the barren wastes of the Falklands. The RAF operates some 33 Chinooks, with one squadron based in the UK and one in Germany.

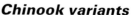

13,400 lb over a 23-mile range or a 6,150-lb load over 115 miles, and the CH-47B and CH-47C models improved on this. The CH-47C, for example, could lift 23,212 lb over a 23-mile range, almost 75 per cent better than the 'A' model. During the 1970s, Boeing Vertol began to progressively upgrade the CH-47C for the export market, introducing a new crashworthy fuel system, an advanced automatic flight control system, uprated transmission, and even a triple cargo hook system rated at 28,000 lb.

Chinook variants

It was inconceivable that the US Army Chinooks would not have these improvements while foreign aircraft did, and in 1979 Boeing flew the first CH-47D, converted from an earlier Chinook variant. The CH-47D also in-

Rotor blades
The glassfibre blades now fitted to RAF Chinooks are able to withstand a hit from a Soviet 23 mm cannon. They have a cambered leading edge, a glassfibre D-section spar and Nomex honeycomb core.

Powerplant
Most RAF Chinooks were originally fitted with Avco Lycoming T55-L-11E turboshafts, but they have now been replaced by improved machinery capable of developing 3,750 hp.

Cockpit
The Chinook has a large cockpit with the captain sitting on the right and co-pilot on the left. Like all RAF and Army Air Corps helicopters, the Chinook carries a precision navigation computer.

Windscreen
The laminated plastic windscreen panels are heated electrically by means of a transparent gold coating.

Centre hook
The centre hook is the main lifting hook, which can carry up to 11,300 kg including such loads as an FH-70 155 mm howitzer.

Main landing gear
The Chinook's four wheel units are not retractable but can be replaced by ski units.

troduced the T55-L-712 engine and a new composite main rotor which together give the aircraft 100 per cent higher performance than the original CH-47A. All the US Army's 436-strong Chinook fleet will eventually be upgraded to CH-47D standard.

The CH-47As and CH-47Bs were converted first, and the new variant entered service in May 1982. The CH-47Cs are initially being updated with glassfibre rotor blades, but will eventually get the full treatment. One hundred and forty-two new-built CH-47Ds were purchased from the late 1980s. Newly-built RAF Chinooks are being delivered to virtually CH-47D specification, and older aircraft have been refitted with the T55-L-712 engine and composite rotors to bring them to this standard.

Plans to acquire the Chinook for the RAF were first formulated in 1967 but were abandoned in 1971 as part of a wide-ranging package of defence cuts. The plans were revived in 1978, and orders were placed for 30 aircraft to enter service from 1980. This was later increased to 33 aircraft, and the three aircraft lost in the Falklands have also been replaced. Plans to order a substantial second batch of Chinooks were abandoned in 1987, in favour of an order for the Anglo-Italian EH-101 Merlin, which may be dubbed 'Griffon' in its RAF form.

RAF use
The Chinook equips two full RAF squadrons, one of which served with BAOR in Germany. One flight of the Odiham-based No. 7 Squadron oper-

An RAF Chinook in the Lebanon as part of the British contingent of the ill-fated multinational peacekeeping force. The large Union Jack gave trigger-happy locals no chance of mistaking a British aircraft for one of the more usual targets.

Above: An RAF Chinook delivers a 155-mm FH-70 gun on exercise. The CH-47 is the only helicopter in NATO capable of lifting such major ordnance and it can carry up to three 105-mm light guns.

programming the TANS, monitoring the engines and assisting the pilot with his lookout. The two crewmen are responsible for loading and un-loading the aircraft, reconfiguring the cabin to suit different types of load, supervising parachute drops and acting as extra pairs of eyes to maintain adequate clearance from the ground or from other obstructions.

Surprisingly agile

The Chinook always looks very slow and cumbersome from the ground, with its huge rotors slowly rotating to give a ponderous chopping beat. It is actually surprisingly fast and agile for a helicopter of its size, but it would still be very vulnerable to ground fire, SAMs or enemy fighters, so it would not usually be committed too close to the FEBA. Even well behind the front line there will always be threats, from roving enemy aircraft to small groups of ground forces who have broken through. In wartime, tactical low-level flying at high speed, down 'among the weeds', will be essential.

Where the ground threat is most important, the Chinook will be manoeuvred hard to avoid skylining, with frequent turns to follow every contour, but where the air threat is predominant straight lines will be flown, to minimise glint from rapidly tilting rotor blades or canopies. Second-hand radar warning receivers have been fitted to the RAF's Chinooks, and trials have been conducted with chaff and flare dispensers. Chinook pilots often practise fighter evasion, sometimes with the aircrewmen

The one Chinook which survived the attack on the Atlantic Conveyor performed sterling service throughout the Falklands conflict, lifting loads which no other helicopter could manage.

ates in support of the UKMF for any out-of-area operations, while the other flight would have reinforced the West German-based No. 18 Squadron in support of I British Corps in time of war. Half of the Falklands-based No. 78 Squadron is also Chinook-equipped, the other flight operating Westland Sea Kings. All the RAF's Chinook units are based at fixed air-fields during peacetime, but would deploy into the field to operate alongside the army in time of war. The Chinook force could operate from various types of site, depending on the nature of the threat, either urban or rural, large or small. They would often be adjacent to a battalion in reserve, to give good guard availability.

Since the Falklands war the RAF's Chinooks have also been used in Northern Ireland and in support of British elements of the UN peacekeeping force in the Lebanon, during 1983 and 1984. The CH-47 saw extensive service during the Gulf War, most being operated by the US Army, but with the RAF contributing a squadron of 15 aircraft to the war effort. The Chinook has had a massive impact on the whole concept of air-mobile operations.

The aircraft is usually operated by a four-man crew, consisting of two pilots and two crewmen. Sometimes one of the pilots is replaced by a navigator, who flies in the left-hand seat and functions as a 'pilot's assistant',

These large rubber balls are fuel bladders being delivered during US Army exercises in west Germany. The US Chinook fleet is over 400 strong and is currently being modernised by the addition of new engines and glassfibre rotor blades.

positioned on the open ramp and in the bubble window to give a more effective lookout in the pilot's blind-spots. If enemy fighters are active, the Chinook will fly at about 90 knots, which is fast enough to spoil anyone's aim, but slow enough for the helicopter to be able to stop or accelerate very quickly or to turn on a sixpence.

The Chinook has given the army a support helicopter of unequalled versatility and capability. Continuing development of the airframe, engines, avionics and tactics will keep it in the front line for years to come.

HELICOPTER COMBAT RESCUE

Taking a helicopter to rescue one of your own pilots behind enemy lines is incredibly risky and demanding. All air forces have helicopter rescue crews who receive training for survival in conditions ranging from the leech-infested heat of the tropics to the bitter cold of the Arctic, all of this whilst coping with an enemy's defences to bring off a behind-the-lines rescue. Among the crew's obvious concerns is to make certain that the rescue succeeds and that the crew – and helicopter – do not themselves become casualties!

A typical rescue helicopter crew consists of pilot, co-pilot and two para-rescue specialists, sometimes called Para-Jumpers, or PJs. All of these men must be disciplined, alert and resourceful.

A rescue mission is about to begin. One of your pilots has been hit over the enemy's territory. After ejecting and parachuting into a low gully not far from enemy troops, he uses his hand-held beeper (actually, a small voice radio) to report his position to friendly forces.

If any doubt exists that this really is the downed pilot, members of the airborne command post in the region – likely to be a C-130 Hercules transport – will ask the man on the ground questions that have been arranged in advance: "What is your mother's maiden name?" "Where did you go to school?" This information on all pilots has already been given to your rescue units. In the immediacy of a battle, there is usually no doubt, but if the enemy is suspected of using an impostor to lure rescue forces, a Q and A session will tell you of the ruse.

An HH-60A helicopter of the US Air Force, modern-day successor to the HH-53s which were used in Vietnam to rescue shot-down aircrew from the North Vietnamese or Viet Cong.

During land hoist training, a para-rescueman or PJ simulates the rescue of a wounded survivor who will be hoisted to the rescue in a litter.

Wearing the maroon beret which distinguishes these elite air crew, a para-rescueman checks the rescue hoist on an HH-53E 'Jolly Green Giant'.

HELICOPTERS AT WAR

Vulnerability
The thin metal skin of a helicopter can be pierced by a ball-point pen if it is slammed against the fuselage in a cupped hand. A single accurate burst from an enemy machine-gun can bring down the helicopter and increase the number of aircrew needing to be rescued.

Head-on target
Above all, the helicopter crew must avoid presenting their extremely vulnerable frontal arc to the enemy. The glass canopy is the helicopter's weakest spot and the route in and out of the rescue site must be carefully chosen to avoid known or likely enemy concentrations.

Second helicopter
Because helicopters are so easily damaged it makes sense to send in rescue helicopters in pairs. The 'Alpha' chopper is the primary helicopter; the 'Bravo' is the back-up.

Para-rescueman
Although their primary purpose is to save lives, these men may have to fight the enemy in order to bring about a successful rescue. Para-rescuemen have to be able to use anything from a Colt .45 to an M-16 rifle and the 7.62-mm Minigun carried on the rescue helicopter.

Pilot's choice
At the rescue site, if weather, terrain conditions and the enemy's strength and location make it possible for him to attempt a pick-up, the pilot must make the final decision whether to go in.

Improvised codes
The enemy may be able to listen to radio messages between a downed pilot and the rescue team. One solution is to use double talk: some frame of reference they cannot understand. One rescue team used the layout of a golf course they and the pilot knew to describe where the downed airmen should go next to avoid the encircling Viet Cong.

With a combat rescue mission now about to unfold, the C-130 command post is joined by tankers (to refuel aircraft in the rescue force) and fighters (to cover the rescue helicopter during its mission). Electronic warfare aircraft may also be operating in the vicinity, foiling the enemy's radar while his ground troops beat through the bush searching for the survivor.

Crew responsibility

Hundreds of people, including ground communicators, may be involved in the rescue attempt. But in the end, success or failure will rest in the hands of the helicopter's crew. The noisy, shuddering, very uncomfortable helicopter will be within a short distance of the enemy and it will be important for each man to check and double-check his readiness.

The pilot is always in command and is responsible for the helicopter's role in the mission, including the decision to abort if there is a mechanical problem or if he suffers battle damage. He must not forget one of the fundamentals of aviation, namely a thorough pre-flight check of the helicopter before taking off. This may be performed by someone else, but it is the pilot's reputation on the line.

The co-pilot

The co-pilot provides a second pair of eyes and ears, as well as a hand on the throttle. The pilot may ask him to handle the controls at critical periods during the mission. He should not forget to keep glancing at the pilot, to make certain he is unhurt, in control and in command. The co-pilot may handle some of the communications with other elements of the rescue force. He will usually have a solid knowledge of the flying characteristics of the helicopter and be pre-

CREW POSITIONS IN AN HH-60 RESCUE HELICOPTER

Para-rescueman 1 operates the hoist and one Minigun

Pilot and co-pilot in armoured seats

Para-rescueman 2 operates port Minigun

CREW POSITIONS IN AN HH-53C RESCUE HELICOPTER

arc of fire of forward Minigun

Para-rescueman 1 operates the rescue hoist and the Minigun from the starboard door

arc of fire of rear Minigun

Pilot and co-pilot sit in 'butterfly' wrap-around armoured seats

Para-rescueman 2 operates the radio and a Minigun which fires through the lowered door in the helicopter's belly

pared to assume the pilot-in-command job if the pilot is disabled or killed by enemy fire.

An elite breed of para-rescue specialists is essential to any rescue force. They are trained in parachuting, helicopter rescue work, and survival in a variety of conditions. They also receive first-aid training and are expected to keep up to date on ways to provide medical help to a survivor.

Two rescuemen

The helicopter carries two such rescuemen, usually a senior non-commissioned officer (NCO) and a more junior airman. The two men should remember to carefully inspect each other's gear to make certain that parachutes are properly packed and equipment properly slung, so that they can use their equipment with maximum ease and comfort. A small error in the fit of a strap supporting a bulky item such as a parachute or medical kit could cause serious injury.

If their mission is to rescue a survivor at sea, the men may make use of their training in parachuting into the sea while equipped with SCUBA (self-contained underwater breathing apparatus). If their rescue is to take place under Polar or Arctic conditions, a scrupulous check must be made of the bulky boots, coveralls, parkas and other gear essential to survival.

Into the mission

On the way towards enemy territory, where the downed pilot is in radio contact and hoping to be picked up before the enemy can take him prisoner, two rescue helicopters in communication with a flying command post approach at low altitude. They are called the 'Alpha bird' (the primary helicopter for the rescue) and the 'Bravo bird' (a back-up).

Experience has shown that sending one helicopter alone, into a region where the enemy may have ground troops, surface-to-air missiles (SAMs) and other defences, is simply not practical. The chances of being shot down with loss of crew are bad enough, but even greater is the prospect of at least minor damage from enemy fire. Having two helicopters provides flexibility.

Talking to the pilot

The survivor now communicates directly with the helicopter pilot as the 'Alpha bird' and 'Bravo bird' approach him. Fighter pilots flying cover, or one of the helicopter pilots, may see a better way to position the survivor for a rescue. If enemy ground troops are approaching through a thick forest to the north, they may direct the survivor to hike towards a riverbank to the south, where a rescue can be attempted with less exposure to enemy fire.

A present-day para-rescueman wears his full kit for a combat rescue with his Sikorsky H-60 helicopter in the background. The oxygen mask will enable him to leap into the area from over 3000 metres. He will free-fall until the last possible moment, using his altimeter to judge opening time.

The crew tries to communicate with the survivor using double-talk, so that he will understand and the enemy, who may be monitoring communications, won't. During the Vietnam War, one downed pilot was given directions to move towards a safer area by using the numbers of his birth date to describe compass headings. The survivor understood, but eavesdropping enemy radiomen did not.

In the Vietnam conflict the PJ was essentially 'married' to the helicopter and would leave it only at the immediate scene of a rescue. In recent times, more flexible tactics have been developed. The helicopter pilot may drop a rescue specialist, by hoist or by parachute, some as distant as 10 miles from the survivor with instructions to trek overland and reach the survivor before the helicopter appears to expose itself at the rescue site.

Wounded survivor

If the survivor is injured or wounded the rescue expert may be able to administer first aid to render him more mobile, so that he can be moved to a location where terrain or the enemy's position is more favourable for a pick-up.

When the weather allows the two-ship helicopter force to 'ingress' the area where the survivor is hoping for rescue, when friendly fighters have delayed the enemy's troops and suppressed his ground fire, and when the survivor is finally in a location where a rescue attempt can be made, everything boils down to the judgement and decision-making abilities of the four men in the helicopter.

Some actual case histories have been far from total successes. In one well-known rescue operation, the enemy succeeded in hiding several machine-gun positions near the survivor. Enemy troops were close enough to seize the survivor but wanted, instead, to use him as bait for the rescue helicopter. Sadly, the enemy's trick worked. Just as the chopper was hovering overhead and lowering the

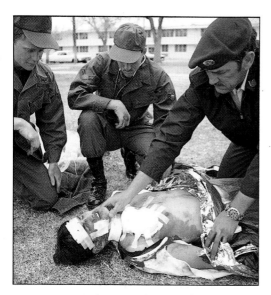

SMSGT Jim Spears, one of the US Air Force's most experienced para-rescuemen, instructs trainees in medical techniques. Unless a casualty is stabilised before evacuation he is likely to die even if successfully rescued.

rescue hoist, the machine-guns opened up. The helicopter was shot down and three of its four crewmen, along with the original survivor, were captured. Only one of the helicopter crew, a para-rescueman, evaded the enemy and was eventually rescued by another helicopter.

Vietnam War

In Vietnam, all sorts of tricks were attempted. A Vietnamese communist soldier was dressed in the standard K2B American flight coveralls, positioned high on a ridgetop with a signal mirror, and instructed to act like a downed American pilot. This deception fooled the rescue forces for only a brief time, but this caused one of the helicopters to become bait for a MiG fighter lurking nearby, the only time in the entire war a MiG shot down an HH-53C chopper, with the loss of all on board.

Miniguns

More often, diligence and perseverance by the helicopter crew pay off. Using communications to guide the survivor to a reasonably safe pick-up site, your rescue crew reaches him before the enemy can. The value of the Miniguns aboard the rescue helicopter should not be overlooked, either. While a direct confrontation is best avoided, those guns can lay down a withering stream of fire on a small unit of enemy soldiers. In the case of today's rescue, the guns are not needed: your PJ lowers himself on a sling, clutches the survivor in a bear hug, and lifts him to safety.

Left: The moment the rescue helicopter is at its most vulnerable – hovering low to pick up the downed pilot. During the Vietnam War the North Vietnamese frequently mounted ambushes for the US rescue teams, positioning heavy machine-guns near a soldier dressed like an American pilot.

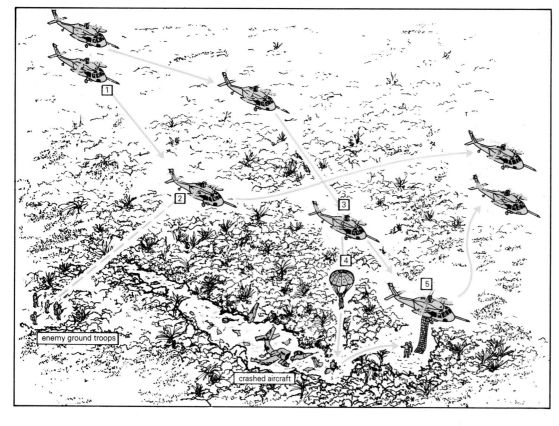

enemy ground troops

crashed aircraft

HOW A RESCUE WORKS

The rescue mission uses a pair of helicopters in case one of them is hit by groundfire and has to abort. Accompanying aircraft engage enemy ground troops while the para-rescueman is dropped to reach the survivor and guide him to the nearest usable landing zone that is not under enemy fire.

1 Flight of two rescue helicopters arrives.

2 'Bravo bird' joins fighter-bombers in suppressing enemy ground troops near the survivor.

3 'Alpha bird' moves in for the rescue.

4 'Alpha bird' drops para-rescueman by hoist or parachute.

5 Para-rescueman reaches the survivor and guides him to the chosen landing zone.

1st SPECIAL OPERATIONS WING USAF

General H. Norman Schwarzkopf was deep into the planning stage of Operation Desert Storm when he called for Air Force Colonel George A. Gray III. Gray was asked whether the MH-53E helicopters from his 1st Special Operations Wing could guarantee the success of a vital mission. Schwarzkopf was reassured by the Air Force man's response, and reportedly said, "Okay, Colonel, you get to start the war."

In the early morning of 17 January 1991, two pairs of USAF MH-53J Pave Low helicopters took off from a Saudi airfield, each pair in company with four AH-64 Apache attack helicopters of the US Army's 1st Battalion, 101st Aviation Brigade. Their task was to simultaneously attack and destroy two air-defence radar sites, 22 and 37 kilometres inside Iraq. By knocking out the overlapping coverage from the two sites, the raid was to create a 'radar black' corridor in Iraq's air defences through which coalition air power would pour in an overwhelming assault on Iraq's command and control infrastructure.

The Sikorsky-built Pave Low had been designed for covert penetration missions, and its sophisticated long-range navigation equipment ensured that the Apache teams could reach the radar sites within 30 seconds of each other.

At 02.38 that morning, the attack went in, the Apaches successfully using Hellfire missiles, 2.75-in rockets and 30-mm gunfire to create the required hole in the Iraqi defences. All aircraft returned safely, but not before the big Sikorskys had used flares to decoy heat-seeking shoulder-fired surface-to-air missiles away from the force. Little has been said about the vital contribution the Pave Low helicopters made to the success of the mission, but that is about par for the course where Special Operations are concerned.

Creature from the swamp

The 1st Special Operations Wing forms part of the US Air Force's Special Operations Command, headquartered at Hurlburt Field in Florida. The wing was deployed to the Gulf in force. Among the units under Colonel Gray's command were the 8th Special Operations Squadron with its MC-130E Combat Talons, the 9th Special Operations Squadron supporting the rest of the wing with its HC-130H Combat Shadow tankers, the 16th Special Operations Squadron equipped with AC-130H Spectre gunships, the 20th Special Operations Squadron with its MH-53J Pave Low helicopters, and the 55th Special Operations Squadron, flying MH-60 Pave Hawk helicopters.

Operation Desert Storm began when MH-53 Pave Low helicopters of 1st SOW flew along a desert wadi, below Iraqi radar, guiding Army AH-64 Apache gunships to two vital radar sites.

Little has been released about the wing's operations in the Gulf, nor of the 39th Special Operations Wing which is normally part of the USAF's European Command and operated out of Turkey during the war. That is how Special Operations personnel like it, since one normally only hears about them when things go wrong. On this occasion, nearly everything went right, although there was one tragedy when an AC-130 with 14 crew members on board was shot down during the battle to retake the Saudi town of Khafji.

15,000-lb bombs

The specialists of the 1st Special Operations Wing undertook a wide range of operations. The four MC-130E Combat Talons of the 8th Special Operations Squadron became an honorary Bomb Squadron when they began to drop BLU-82 'Daisy Cutter' bombs. Flying at 17,000 ft or more, they managed to get the bombs to within 50 ft of the aim points. When one considers that a BLU-82 weighs some 15,000 pounds, and 12,600 pounds of that is high explosive, that is as good as a direct hit.

Initially used to blast through Iraqi border defences, the huge bombs had a dramatic effect. One British SAS team, observing an explosion from many miles away, thought that a tacti-

Right: 1st SOW played a vital role during the Gulf War, particularly in the 'Scud' hunt across western Iraq. MH-53 helicopters worked with Army Special Forces far behind enemy lines.

Below: The 1st SOW's heaviest firepower is provided by Lockheed AC-130s armed with 20-mm cannon, a 40-mm Bofors and a 105-mm howitzer. One was shot down during the battle for Khafji.

cal nuclear device had been detonated, and an advancing infantry unit found that every Iraqi within three miles of the blast had been killed. The Combat Talons also dropped more than 17 million leaflets in the course of 40 sorties.

MC-130s also flew tanker missions for the MH-53J Pave Low helicopters of the 20th Special Operations Squadron. After taking part in the first official mission of the war, the 20th went on to fly more than 60 missions behind enemy lines. The squadron's MH-53Js were heavily involved in the campaign to find and neutralise Iraqi 'Scud' missiles, using their night vision systems to seek out mobile 'Scud' launchers while inserting and extracting Special Forces ground

teams. One such team found 29 'Scuds' ready to fire at Israel less than two days before the end of the war. The site was blasted by Air Force A-10s.

Special Operations Forces were also responsible for combat rescue operations in the Gulf. In this they took the place of the Air Force's Air Rescue Service, which was not deployed, although numbers of ARS personnel did serve in the Kuwait Theater of Operations. The Special Operations helicopters managed a few rescues, the first being performed by the 20th SOS, who picked up a downed Navy F-14 pilot. It was a close thing, however, since the helicopter had to take out two Iraqi trucks closing in on the pilot.

Mi-24

RIDING THE DEVIL'S CHARIOT

The Mi-24 'Hind' has been widely exported to a wide range of Soviet client states, and is an important front-line aircraft in most of the world's trouble spots. Although not invulnerable to intensive ground fire, it has impressed most of those who have come up against it with its toughness and firepower. 'Hind' has been used in anger by Iraq during the war with Iran, by Angola against the South African-backed UNITA guerrillas and by Nicaragua against rebel right-wing Contra guerrillas, as well as by the Soviet and Afghan air forces in Afghanistan.

This type of Third World counter-insurgency fighting, however, does not give a true idea of the role for which 'Hind' was designed. The Soviet Union realised the military potential of the helicopter at a relatively early stage, seeing beyond the limited roles assigned to British, French and American helicopters in Malaya, Cyprus, Algeria and Vietnam.

Expendable weapons

The helicopter is inherently vulnerable over a modern battlefield, but Soviet willingness to accept heavy losses allowed their air force planners to view the helicopter virtually as an airborne tank, being heavily armed and yet able to move swiftly over the battlefield, regardless of terrain.

By the mid-1960s the Soviets were developing a new assault helicopter able to carry an eight-man infantry or anti-tank squad, well-armoured and

Above: Mi-24s of the East German air force are seen on exercise shortly before the collapse of the Warsaw Pact.

Below: Maintenance work on an East German Mi-24. Note the 12.7-mm, four-barrelled machine-gun under the nose.

packing the biggest possible punch to allow offensive operations over enemy territory.

The Mi-24 is loosely based on the Mi-8 'Hip' transport helicopter, although it has more powerful engines and smaller rotor blades. The whole fuselage was redesigned to give a smaller cabin and a slimmer cross-section. The four-man crew, comprising two pilots, a navigator and a gunner, sit under a streamlined canopy, with the pilots to the rear. Early 'Hinds' set an impressive number of world speed records, and the type was in front-line service by 1974, receiving the NATO code-name 'Hind-A'.

'Hind-A' was an impressive machine by any standards, with its nose-mounted 12.7-mm cannon, underwing rocket pods and radio-guided AT-2 'Swatter' anti-tank missiles and heavy armour, but it was soon superseded by the even more capable 'Hind-D'. This new version featured a new forward fuselage housing a new two-man cockpit and a baffling array of sophisticated sensors. A new four-barrel Gatling-type 12.7-mm rotary cannon was installed in a chin-mounted turret, and new low-light television, radar, forward-looking infra-red and laser sensors were also fitted.

Long-range missile

The laser, mounted on the port wingtip, was associated with the new AT-6 'Spiral' laser-guided, tube-launched anti-tank missile. 'Spiral' is believed to have an effective range of up to 5000 metres. This long range allows 'Hind-D' to engage tanks while remaining well beyond the effective range of their armament. 'Hind-D' was also structurally strengthened, with stronger rotor blades and increased titanium content in the airframe.

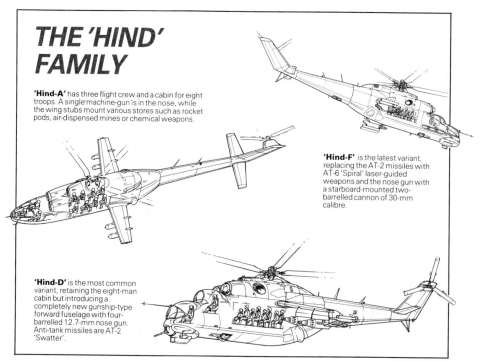

THE 'HIND' FAMILY

'Hind-A' has three flight crew and a cabin for eight troops. A single machine-gun is in the nose, while the wing stubs mount various stores such as rocket pods, air-dispensed mines or chemical weapons.

'Hind-F' is the latest variant, replacing the AT-2 missiles with AT-6 'Spiral' laser-guided weapons and the nose gun with a starboard-mounted two-barrelled cannon of 30-mm calibre.

'Hind-D' is the most common variant, retaining the eight-man cabin but introducing a completely new gunship-type forward fuselage with four-barrelled 12.7-mm nose gun. Anti-tank missiles are AT-2 'Swatter'.

Above: This Mi-24 has two rocket pods fitted under its wings. The pods carry 32 S-5 unguided 57-mm rockets, with a maximum range of 1200 metres.

Mi-24s take part in an amphibious exercise in the Baltic. There is no naval version of the 'Hind', the East German, Soviet and Polish forces in the Baltic relied on land-based aircraft and helicopters to support the fleet.

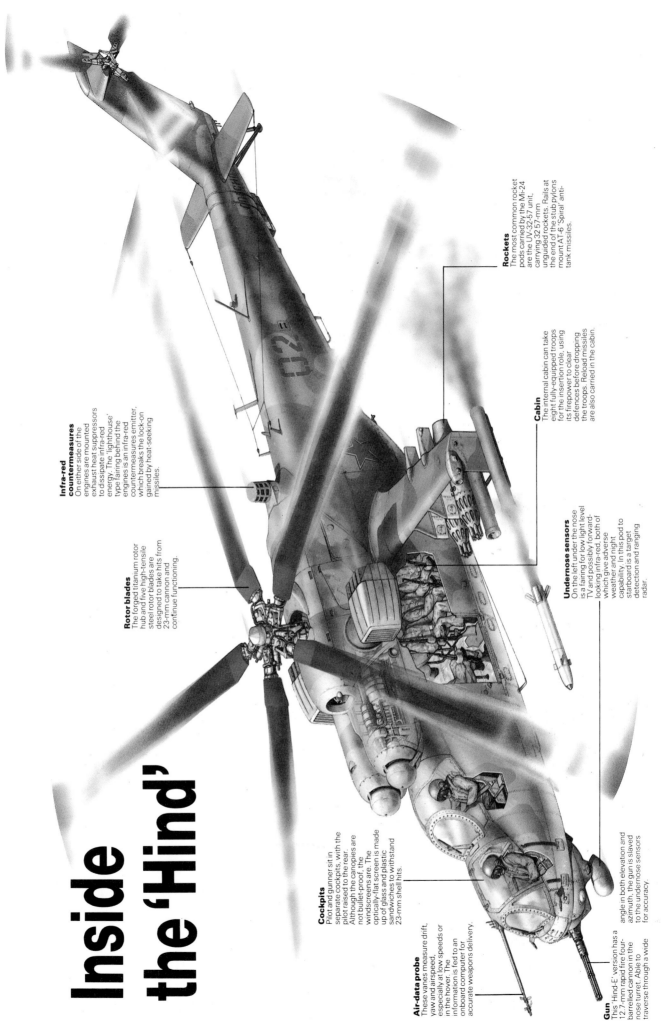

Inside the 'Hind'

Infra-red countermeasures
On either side of the engines are mounted exhaust heat suppressors to dissipate infra-red energy. The 'lighthouse' type fairing behind the engines is an infra-red countermeasures emitter, which breaks the lock-on gained by heat-seeking missiles.

Rotor blades
The forged titanium rotor hub and five high-tensile steel rotor blades are designed to take hits from 23-mm cannon and continue functioning.

Rockets
The most common rocket pods carried by the Mi-24 are the UV-32-57 unit, carrying 32 57-mm unguided rockets. Rails at the end of the stub pylons mount AT-6 'Spiral' anti-tank missiles.

Cabin
The internal cabin can take eight fully-equipped troops for the insertion role, using its firepower to clear defences before dropping the troops. Reload missiles are also carried in the cabin.

Undernose sensors
On the left under the nose is a fairing for low light level TV and possibly forward-looking infra-red, both of which give adverse weather and night capability. In this pod to starboard is a target detection and ranging radar.

Cockpits
Pilot and gunner sit in separate cockpits, with the pilot raised to the rear. Although the canopies are not bullet-proof, the windscreens are. The optically-flat screen is made up of glass and plastic sandwiches to withstand 23-mm shell hits.

Air-data probe
These vanes measure drift, yaw and airspeed, especially at low speeds or in the hover. The information is fed to an onboard computer for accurate weapons delivery.

Gun
This 'Hind-E' version has a 12.7-mm rapid fire four-barrelled cannon in the nose turret. Able to traverse through a wide angle in both elevation and azimuth, the gun is slaved to the undernose sensors for accuracy.

This Afghan Mi-24 carries rocket pods but without the guided anti-tank missiles fitted to the outer rail. The Mujahideen called the helicopter the 'Devil's Chariot'.

'Hind-D' is now an important part of Soviet Frontal Aviation, and would be extensively used in the intensive, co-ordinated fixed-wing and rotary-wing air operations that would accompany any thrust by the ground forces. The main aims of such Soviet air operations would include the destruction of enemy aircraft and helicopters, and their crews, on the ground or in the air.

The Mi-24 'Hind' is used in conjunction with fixed-wing close-support aircraft. Tactics involving the coordinated use of fast jets and 'Hinds' have been developed and refined during the long war in Afghanistan, and the Sukhoi Su-25 'Frogfoot' has emerged as a particularly useful complement to the 'Hind', acting as an escort and defence suppression aircraft.

Mi-24s usually operate in flights of four, sub-divided into pairs for mutual support. The two flights can then make co-ordinated attacks from different directions, or one flight can attack while the other draws enemy fire. Like Western helicopters, the Mi-24s generally transit to their targets flying close to the ground ('nap-of-the-earth') making maximum use of terrain cover to avoid exposure to enemy radar.

Diving attack

Where defensive fire is light the 'Hind' can make a diving attack from about 1000 metres, allowing it to deliver its weapon load with extreme accuracy before breaking into evasive terrain-hugging flight. This sort of attack profile is ideally suited to the delivery of free-fall bombs, unguided rockets, or for strafe attacks.

The latest major Mi-24 variant, dubbed 'Hind-F' by NATO, has its chin-turret-mounted 12.7-mm cannon replaced by a twin-barrelled 23-mm cannon fixed to the starboard forward fuselage. The standard S-5 57-mm rocket has a HEAT shaped-charge warhead capable of penetrating 220 mm of armour and a range in excess of 1200 metres. Rockets, cannon or anti-tank guided missiles can be fired while the helicopter is hovering, popping up from behind cover to fire.

The success of the 'Hind' has led to the development of a new generation of attack helicopters such as the Mi-28 'Havoc' and Kamov 'Hokum', dedicated gunships with no troop-carrying capability but with superb manoeuvrability, thick armour and sophisticated weapons.

This Polish Mi-24 is camouflaged in exactly the same way as the Afghan 'Hind' above and the East German one on page 13. The colours vary but the pattern is identical, presumably because the Soviets supply a standard mask.

HELICOPTER WEAPONS

Since their battlefield debut during the Korean War combat helicopters have come a long way. First provided with sophisticated armaments by the French in Algeria, the armed helicopter came of age during the Vietnam War. Attack helicopters now bristle with advanced electronic and electro-optical equipment, and they carry a wide range of enormously potent armament which would have been beyond the wildest dreams of the helicopter pioneers.

The early machines were fragile, unarmed, poorly-powered devices, being used primarily as transports or on medevac missions. However, it was not long before military planners wanted to use the type's unique capabilities in a true fighting machine.

It was not a question of simply putting guns aboard, however. Even today, for fundamental reasons of aerodynamics, structural stress, induced vibration and metal fatigue,

Above: The awesome armoury of the AH-64 Apache includes air-to-air missiles, 76 70-mm rockets, 1,200 30-mm cannon shells and 16 Hellfire missiles.

Below: A doorgunner returns fire on North Vietnamese troops. The 'Razorbacks' were part of the US 1st Air Cavalry in Vietnam.

helicopters are much slower than equivalent conventional aircraft and are generally considered more vulnerable. It was much more so in the years after World War II, when the first practical rotary-winged aircraft were produced.

Those first armed helicopters were used for simple experiments with machine-guns, air-to-surface rockets and anti-submarine weapons. In general, these have remained the main categories of helicopter weapons, but early helicopters were simply not practical weapons carriers. Even the best designs had very small payloads, and it was impossible to carry a worthwhile weapons load without sacrificing mission radius or endurance. It was the French in Algeria who first used armed helicopters extensively. Initially they simply placed machine-guns in the doorways, and simple air-to-ground rockets followed.

Gas-turbine propulsion

The turning point in the evolution of the armed helicopter came at the end of the 1950s, with the switch to gas-turbine propulsion. Smaller, lighter, but vastly more powerful than conventional piston engines used until then, the gas turbine at a stroke enabled the helicopter to move faster, further, with heavier loads. At the same time, safety and reliability were improved and twin-engined safety became possible.

The Vietnam War was the great testing ground for the armed helicopter. There were no fixed fighting lines and the enemy was small and elusive. The helicopter's unique abilities made American mobile tactics possible, especially when the clumsy machines used in the early days were replaced by the neat, powerful and flexible Bell UH-1 'Huey'.

Originally designed as a light transport, the UH-1 soon sprouted a variety

Even light scout helicopters like this Hughes 500 can now carry powerful anti-tank missiles such as the Hughes TOW system.

of weapons, from door-mounted machine-guns through flex guns and six-barrelled Miniguns to a variety of rockets. The UH-1 also formed the basis for the AH-1 Cobra, the first true gunship. This had everything that the earlier helicopter had, plus cannon and 40-mm grenade launchers.

Other countries were slow to follow the gunship concept, but they were not slow in arming helicopters. The French followed their pioneering efforts with an even more important step. They mated the new lightweight wire-guided anti-tank missile, like the SS-11 then being developed, with the small turbine-powered helicopter to produce a highly effective and mobile tank killer.

The pace of helicopter weapons development has been hectic. As new missiles have been developed, equally new helicopters with advanced electronic, radar and infra-red sensors have also appeared to fire them. The Hughes TOW was used at the end of the Vietnam War and was for many years to come a standard NATO anti-tank weapon. The Franco-German HOT is a very similar system.

Missile-armed helicopters range from the tiny McDonnell 300 and 500 series through such types as the Aérospatiale Gazelle and Westland Lynx to big machines such as the Soviet Mil Mi-8 'Hip'. It is the specialist gunship which has brought the armed helicopter to its current peak.

The pioneering Cobra is still in service.

The powerful Soviet Mil Mi-24 'Hind' probably first flew in the late 1960s and was converted to a gunship design in the early 1970s. Big, fast and heavily armoured, the 'Hind' carries the original gunship-type armament of machine-guns, cannon and rockets, and has been steadily upgraded with AT-3 'Sagger' wire-guided and AT-6 'Spiral' laser-guided anti-armour missiles. It can also carry and drop conventional bombs.

Potent gunship

The most potent of current gunships is the McDonnell AH-64 Apache. Heavily armoured for survivability over the battlefield, it is armed with a 30-mm Chain Gun and can carry a mix of guns, rockets and Hellfire laser-guided anti-armour missiles. Hellfire is bigger, faster and longer ranged than previous missiles, and the Apache/Hellfire combination was tested in the Gulf War and proved to be a war winner.

In addition to ground attack weapons, combat helicopters like the Apache and its rivals, the Kamov 'Hokum', the Mil 'Havoc' and the Eurocopter Tiger, can all be equipped with air-to-air and anti-radiation missiles.

The future of helicopter weaponry seems assured. Advances in propulsion, weaponry, construction and avionics have led to new breeds of helicopter which can fly reliably in all weathers, deal devastating blows against hostile targets while remaining hidden, yet be surprisingly immune to return fire. From being one of the most vulnerable machines ever to fly, the helicopter has become one of the best protected and, with its advanced armament, one of the most potent of battlefield weapon systems.

The Soviet Mi-24 'Hind' saw extensive action in Afghanistan, where its cannon, rockets and bombs were among the most effective weapons used against the elusive guerrillas.

A spectacular Warsaw Pact amphibious assault exercise includes East German Mi-8 'Hip' helicopters and an 'Aist' class hovercraft of the Soviet Baltic Fleet.

The Mi-8 came from the design bureau of the brilliant Soviet helicopter pioneer Mikhail Leontyevich Mil, who died in 1970. A string of mass-produced and record-breaking helicopters remains the testament to his engineering and design skills. The Mi-8, a turbine-powered development of the Mi-4 'Hound' (itself a shock to the West), was first seen in public at Tushino in 1961 and was powered by a single 2013-kW Soloviev turbine mounted above the cabin roof. Although the fuselage was new, with the pilot's seats at the front instead of over the cabin, the helicopter employed the rotor hub, rotor blades, transmission and boom of the Mi-4. The second prototype, which flew in September 1962, was powered by two 1044-kW Isotov TV2 turboshafts, and the production version was given a five-bladed main rotor in place of the four-blade rotor inherited from the 'Hound'.

The Mi-8's fuselage is a conventional all-metal semi-monocoque structure of the pod and boom type. The tricycle landing gear is non-retractable, with a steerable twin-wheel nose unit which is locked in

Mi-8 'HIP'

A Soviet Mi-8 seen at Moscow's Tushino airport. Western observers first saw the Mi-8 in military colours in 1967. Since then it has been widely exported to Soviet allies.

flight, and a single wheel on each main unit. Two pilots sit side-by side in the cockpit, which also has provision for a flight engineer's seat. The standard passenger version has 28 four-abreast tip-up seats with a centre aisle, a wardrobe and luggage compartment, or 32 seats and bulkheads that are removable for the carriage of cargo. The Mi-8T has cargo tie-down rings on the floor, a winch of 200 kilograms capacity, an external cargo sling system with a capacity of 3000 kilograms, and 24 tip-up seats along the side walls of the cabin. Clamshell freight doors and hook-on ramps facilitate vehicle loading, while a passenger airstair is standard on the commercial version. The Mi-8 Salon (a VIP version for 11 passengers) was demonstrated at the Paris air show in 1971.

NATO reporting name

NATO allocated the reporting names 'Hip-A' and Hip-B' to the prototypes, and at the spectacular 1967 Domodedovo air display the 'Hip' appeared in military colours. Military production was under way, and no time was lost in taking advantage of the Americans' hard-won experience of Vietnam. The 'Hip' became the standard Soviet utility/assault helicopter (able to carry 24 armed troops) and was well to the fore in the Soviet development of the air-mobile concept. Outriggers with two pylons were added on each side of the cabin to carry four UV-32-57 packs, each containing 32 55-mm S-5 air-to-surface rockets. This version was designated 'Hip-C', but by 1979 a more potent variant, the 'Hip-E', had become the world's most heavily-armed helicopter with six UV-32-57 packs housing 192 rockets, four AT-2 'Swatter' anti-tank guided missiles on rails

Inside the 'Hip'

The Mi-8 'Hip' has been supplied to many Soviet allies. This 'Hip' is shown in the colours of the Angolan Communist government that fought the pro-Western UNITA guerrillas from 1975 to 1991. Flown mainly by Cuban mercenaries, the Angolan's Mi-8s started to fall victim to Stinger missiles supplied by the CIA and they became ineffective against an increasingly confident guerrilla army.

Cockpit
The pilots sit side-by-side with a flight engineer behind them. The nose glazing below is fitted with a DShK 12.7-mm machine-gun on the 'Hip-E' version.

above the rocket packs and a nose-mounted 12.7-mm machine-gun. Even when fully fuelled and armed, the 'Hip-E' can still lift 12-14 troops, though operations at maximum gross

weight allow little power for manoeuvre at low speed and in the hover.

Other military versions in use include the 'Hip-D' and 'Hip-G', which have been developed for command and control duties. The 'Hip-D' is similar to the 'Hip-C' but features canisters on the outer stores racks and added antennas for the battlefield communications-relay role, while the 'Hip-G' has rearward inclined antennas projecting from the rear of the cabin and from the undersurface of the tailboom, though intended for the same task as the 'Hip-C'. The 'Hip-F' is an export version of the 'Hip-E' and is equipped with six AT-3 'Saggers' in place of the four 'Swatters'. This version first entered service with the East German 'Adolf von Lützow' Combat Helicopter Regiment. The 'Hip-J' is an ECM version identifiable by additional small boxes on the

The Mi-8 played a key role in the Soviet occupation of Afghanistan between 1979 and 1990. Airborne assault troops were the only units capable of dealing effective blows against the Mujahideen.

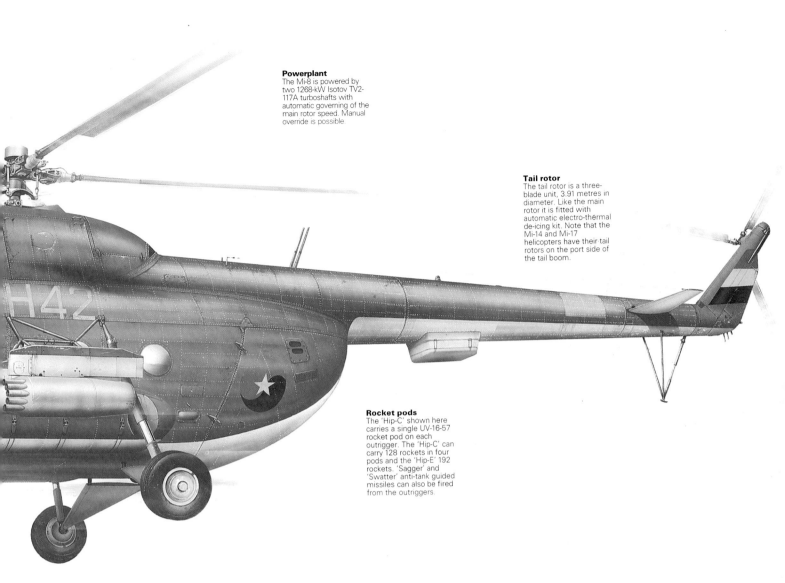

Powerplant
The Mi-8 is powered by two 1268-kW Isotov TV2-117A turboshafts with automatic governing of the main rotor speed. Manual override is possible.

Tail rotor
The tail rotor is a three-blade unit, 3.91 metres in diameter. Like the main rotor it is fitted with automatic electro-thermal de-icing kit. Note that the Mi-14 and Mi-17 helicopters have their tail rotors on the port side of the tail boom.

Rocket pods
The 'Hip-C' shown here carries a single UV-16-57 rocket pod on each outrigger. The 'Hip-C' can carry 128 rockets in four pods and the 'Hip-E' 192 rockets. 'Sagger' and 'Swatter' anti-tank guided missiles can also be fired from the outriggers.

sides of the fuselage, fore and aft of the main landing gear legs. The 'Hip-K' is a communications-jamming ECM version with a large antenna array on each side of the cabin.

Export success

By 1990 some 1,600 Mi-8s were in service with the USSR's Frontal Aviation, 900 with Transport Aviation and a further 100 with Naval Aviation. Mi-8s have also been exported to 39 other countries and have tasted combat in several theatres of action. During the first evening of the Yom Kippur War in 1973 a force of about 100 'Hips' carrying crack 18-man Egyptian commando teams crossed the Suez Canal to attack Israeli oil-fields and to hinder the movement of reinforcements. The commandos were supported by 'Hips' armed with rockets and bombs, while others were modified to carry two fixed heavy machine-guns and up to six light machine-guns to provide suppressive fire around LZs. Napalm bombs were also reported to have been rolled out through the clamshell doors on to Israeli positions along the canal. Egyptian 'Hips' were also used for resupply and medevac duties. The Syrians employed about a dozen 'Hips' to deliver commandos 2440 metres up Mount Hermon to capture an Israeli observation post.

In the bitter Ogaden War, the Soviet commander of the Ethiopian forces used 'Hips' to airlift troops and light armoured vehicles over a mountain and place them behind forward Somali positions. And earlier, in 1974, two Soviet 'Hips' operated from the deck of the ASW helicopter cruiser *Leningrad* as they helped sweep mines from the southern end of the Suez Canal. More recently, 'Hips' have been used both for troop transport and as gunships in the protracted Afghanistan conflict. During the month following the Soviet invasion of Christmas 1979, Mi-8s (some of them from Aeroflot) provided logistic support, and 'Hips' were used extensively throughout the conflict.

Like the Huey 'slicks' and 'hogs' of

An Mi-8 of the East German army fires a salvo of 57-mm rockets. The ability to carry six 57-mm rocket pods gives the Mi-8 unprecedented firepower.

Vietnam, troop-carrying 'Hips' are usually escorted by the more heavily-armed Mi-24 'Hind-D' gunships. It has been claimed in the USA that both these helicopters were used to wage chemical and biological warfare against the Afghan guerrillas, with loads generally fired in 55-mm rocket rounds. But Mi-8s have also been put to humanitarian use. During 1985, for instance, Soviet and Polish 'Hips' took part in famine-relief operations in drought-stricken Ethiopia. The Polish Relief Helicopter Squadron arrived at Assab aboard the MV *Wislica* with 100 tons of food and equipment. Three days later the Mi-8Ts were assembled and began airlifting supplies for distribution to the starving in the desert. In Finland, the Mi-8s of the Finnish air force (Suomen Ilmavoimat) and the Frontier Guard (Rajavartiolaitos) have added a useful dimension to the country's communications network, particularly through the country's long, hard winters when overland routes are blocked by snow or floods.

When the Soviets sought a suitable replacement for the ageing ASW version of the Mi-4 'Hound' they looked no further than the versatile 'Hip', although the conversion proved to be a lengthy affair. The project began in about 1968 and the first flight of the Mi-14 (given the reporting name 'Haze-A' by NATO) did not take place until 1973, indicating some major stumbling blocks. This long overdue ASW helicopter serves only with shore-based elements of Naval Aviation, as it is far too big to use the elevators of the 'Kiev' class carriers and it would be unthinkable for them to remain on deck during a lengthy voyage.

The Mi-14 has shorter engine nacelles than the Mi-8, indicating the use of the uprated TV3-117 turboshafts found on the Mi-17 and Mi-24, and the tail rotor has been relocated to the port side of the fin. Other new

features include a boat-shaped hull (for emergency amphibious operations) with a sponson on each side at the rear of the cabin, and a small float under the boom. The landing gear is fully retractable. A Doppler radar box is housed under the forward part of the boom, while additional equipment includes a search radar beneath the nose and a MAD 'bird' stowed in the angle of the fuselage/boom junction. Torpedoes and depth charges are carried in an enclosed bay at the bottom of the hull.

Friendly users

About 100 Mi-14s are operated by the Russian naval air force, which has retired its fleet of obsolete Mi-4s from shore-based ASW units. The 'Haze-A', which has a crew of four or five, is also in service with the naval forces of Bulgaria, Cuba, Libya, Poland, Romania and Syria.

The 'Haze-B' is a mine countermeasures version, and is identifiable by a fuselage strake and pod on the starboard side of the cabin, and deletion of the sonar 'bird'.

A more powerful and modernised development of the Mi-8 is the Mi-17

The Egyptian forces still operate a large number of Mi-8s, primarily as troop carriers. Syria has also made successful use of heliborne commando troops in Mi-8s.

medium-lift helicopter, which is powered by two 1417-kW Isotov TV3-117MT turboshafts. SSSR-17718, in Aeroflot markings, was first displayed in the West at the Paris air show in 1981. The higher-performance turboshafts give double the previous climb rate, and increase maximum take-off weight from 12000 kilograms to 13000 kilograms. Loss of power by one engine is offset automatically by an increase in the output of the other engine. An APU is standard, while the engine air inlets can be fitted with deflectors for operations in desert or dusty regions.

The military version of the Mi-17 is known as the 'Hip-H', and deliveries have been made to Angola, Cuba, Czechoslovakia and India, in addition to the 150 supplied to Frontal Aviation.

The Indian Air Force operates over 50 Mi-8s in six squadrons. They are used as transports with No. 109 Squadron assigned to carrying VIPs.

The Kamov Ka-25 has been used by the Soviet navy since the 1960s, and over a hundred of these venerable machines were still in service when the USSR finally collapsed in 1991. Operating from aircraft and helicopter carriers, as well as other major surface units, the Ka-25 was used to hunt submarines and to help target long-range missiles.

KAMOV Ka-25

From 1965-75 the USSR manufactured an estimated total of 500 Kamov Ka-25 helicopters. Allotted the NATO reporting name 'Hormone', the Ka-25 was the standard helicopter of the Soviet navy until the introduction of the Ka-27 'Helix' at the end of the 1970s. It is estimated that about 120 'Hormones' remain in service with the former Soviet fleets. The 'Moskva' and 'Kiev' class helicopter carriers operated 14 and 20 'Hormones', respectively, and most major surface warships were equipped with a single 'Hormone' flying from a hangar aft.

All modern Soviet cruisers from the 'Kresta' to the 'Slava' classes carried one Ka-25, as did the 'Sovremenny' class destroyers; the giant *Kirov* (now *Admiral Ushakov*) battle cruiser and her sister ships carry three. While the carrier *Kuznetsov* and the 'Kievs' have received Ka-27 'Helix' helicopters instead, the Ka-25 remained the main Soviet ASW (anti-submarine warfare) helicopter until the collapse of the USSR.

The Ka-25 'Hormone' uses co-axial rotors, which take up less room than a conventional layout – very useful for shipboard helicopters.

The first Soviet warships to carry a helicopter to sea were the three 'Kresta I' class cruisers laid down in 1964-5 and commissioned in 1967-8. These carried the 'Hormone-B' version of the Ka-25, which was used to locate targets for the cruiser's SS-N-3B 'Shaddock' surface-to-surface mis-

siles. The SS-N-3 is command guided with active radar homing in the final stage of its attack. It has a maximum range of 460 kilometres, so it can engage targets far over the horizon and way beyond the range of the 'Kresta's surface-search radar.

With a range of nearly 400 kilo-

metres and fitted with 'Big Bulge' radar, which can detect major surface ships at nearly 200 kilometres, 'Hormone-B' allowed the Soviet cruisers to exploit the full potential of their long-range missiles. The Ka-25 could fly ahead of its parent ship, locate targets and allow the cruiser to fire its missiles from over the visual and radar horizons. 'Hormone-B' still performs such a role aboard some of the latest Soviet warships, e.g. the 'Sovremenny' class destroyers and 'Slava' class cruisers.

Anti-submarine

Unlike the 'Kresta Is', the 10 'Kresta II' class cruisers commissioned from 1968-77 were primarily intended for ASW rather than surface action. In place of the SS-N-3 they carry the SS-N-14 'Silex' missile, which delivers a homing torpedo or nuclear depth charge at up to 55 kilometres. Instead of the unarmed reconnaissance/targeting helicopter, they each operate a 'Hormone-A': the specialist ASW version of the Ka-25. This was an important new platform for the Soviet fleet, which commissioned two specialist ASW helicopter carriers, 'Moskva' and 'Leningrad' in 1967-8, each equipped to operate 14 'Hormone-As'.

The 'Hormone-A' carries a dipping sonar and three sonobuoys to detect submarines. It can either call in a missile/depth charge attack from its parent ship or attack with its own weapons. The normal weapon fit for a 'Hormone-A' is a pair of 450-mm homing torpedoes. These have a reported range of 8000 metres and carry a 90-kilogram warhead capable of sinking or crippling the largest submarines. Alternatively, the 'Hormone-A' can carry a pair of depth charges or a single nuclear depth bomb.

To detect submarines the 'Hormone-A's most effective system is its dipping sonar. Lowered into the water from the hovering helicopter, this actively 'pings' away and will locate submarines within one or two kilometres depending on the sea state. The Ka-25 has no automatic hover facility and so it cannot use its dipping sonar at night or in poor visibility when manual hovering is too dangerous.

Dropping sonobuoys

The sonobuoys have a similar range but can be set for passive operation in which they 'listen' quietly, revealing the bearing of any submarine present. 'Hormone-A' also carries a MAD (Magnetic Anomaly Detector) that will pick up the inevitable disturbance in the magnetic field caused by several hundred tons of steel submarine passing close by.

The Ka-25 is a co-axial helicopter: its two main rotors turn in opposite directions about the same vertical

Left: A Ka-25 heads off from the helicopter carrier Moskva during a deployment to the Mediterranean in the early 1970s.

Crew members run to man their Ka-25s aboard the aircraft carrier Kiev. The dustbin-shaped containers on the side of each helicopter contain three sonobuoys, which are dropped into the sea to locate submarines.

Co-axial rotors
The Kamov Ka-25 is one of the few helicopters in military service to employ co-axial rotors. They are very well suited to shipboard use; the overall length of the helicopter can be relatively short as there is no tail rotor.

Into the wind
Like most naval helicopters, the Ka-25 is launched with the ship steering close into the wind if it is to carry its full weapon load.

The landing gear
This comprises four separate units. The front wheels are carried on vertical long-travel legs and can castor for easy handling on deck. The larger rear wheels are on near-vertical long-stroke struts.

Kamov Ka-25

Allotted the NATO reporting name 'Hormone', the Kamov Ka-25 was carried by most major surface units of the Soviet navy. It is likely to be retired from front-line service soon, as the carriers *Minsk* and *Leningrad* are likely to be scrapped and the future of the others is uncertain.

axis, driven by co-axial shafts. This obviates the need for a tail rotor and helps make the Ka-25 suitably compact for shipboard operation. The rotors are made from aluminium alloy and have a large gap between them to ensure they never touch. The fuselage is also light alloy, with the cockpit in the nose running the full width of the machine and the two pilots seated side by side. There is a small sliding door either side of the cockpit and a large sliding door on the left of the helicopter leading to the main cabin.

The wheel units can be fitted with rapid-inflating flotation bags in case the Ka-25 comes down over water. Although not designed for amphibious operation, some Ka-25s have survived water landings and been returned to service. The Ka-25 has two turbo-shaft engines with heating and de-icing systems to keep the helicopter operational in extreme cold. The fuel tank is underneath the cabin floor. 'Hormone-A' has four crew: two pilots and two men to operate the ASW systems from the cabin. In addition to the 'Big Bulge' radar, it carries a radar altimeter to monitor its height above the sea, an IFF system and secure data-link to its parent ship.

Below: A Ka-25 lowers its dipping sonar to listen for a NATO submarine. This type of sonar can only detect submarines within a few thousand metres.

Compared with other naval helicopters, the Ka-25's main handicap is its relatively modest range. Veteran Western equivalents like the Royal Navy Wessexes that were retired in the 1980s had longer range, and those in service with most NATO navies today are far more capable machines.

Only a few 'Hormones' were exported. The Indian navy has five 'Kashin' class destroyers, each with one Ka-25 'Hormone-A'. Syria used to operate another five 'Hormone-As' from bases ashore; although these have since been replaced with Ka-27s, the earlier machines may still be operational. Vietnam is reported to operate some 13 land-based 'Hormone-As', and the former Yugoslav navy had 15 'Hormone-As' to provide ASW support to its five locally-built diesel-electric submarines.

Soviet sailors stripped to the waist surround a line of Ka-25s aboard a 'Kiev' class aircraft carrier off the Libyan coast. Note the single Yak-36 STOL aircraft in the middle.